WORDLY WISE 3000®
SECOND EDITION

Book 8

Kenneth Hodkinson | Sandra Adams

EDUCATORS PUBLISHING SERVICE
Cambridge and Toronto

Original cover design: Hugh Price
Interior design: Sarah Cole
Acquisitions/Development: Kate Moltz
Editors: Wendy Drexler, Elissa Gershowitz, Stacey Nichols Kim, Theresa Trinder, Laura Woollett
Editorial Assistant: Becky Ticotsky
Senior Editorial Manager: Sheila Neylon

Printed in Westford, MA, in June 2011
ISBN 978-0-8388-2826-7

11 12 13 CRW 14 13 12 11

Contents

Lesson 1. 1
A Poet of the People 6

Lesson 2. 9
The Iceman. 14

Lesson 3. 17
Telling Tales 22

Lesson 4. 25
The Tiger's Whisker 30

Review for Lessons 1–4. 34

Lesson 5. 35
The Bounty, Part One. 39

Lesson 6. 43
The Bounty, Part Two 47

Lesson 7. 51
Women in Space, Part One 56

Lesson 8. 59
Women in Space, Part Two 64

Review for Lessons 5–8. 67

Lesson 9. 70
The Children of the Bounty. 75

Lesson 10. 78
Rigoberta Menchu 83

Lesson 11 86
The Kachina Dolls of Oraibi 91

Lesson 12. 94
Hearst Castle's Master Builder 99

Review for Lessons 9–12. 102

Lesson 13 103
More Than Just a Pretty Flower. 107

Lesson 14 111
Leonardo da Vinci: Renaissance Man .116

Lesson 15 119
Who's Afraid of the Big, Bad Wolf? . . 124

Lesson 16 127
The Wisdom of Rabbi Rabinowicz . . . 131

Review for Lessons 13–16. 135

Lesson 17 138
The Country Without an Army 143

Lesson 18 146
Prairie Women 151

Lesson 19 154
The Thousand-Year Battle. 159

Lesson 20 162
Paul Robeson: All-American 167

Review for Lessons 17–20. 170

Lesson 1

Word List

Study the definitions of the words below; then do the exercises for the lesson.

avid
av´ id

adj. 1. Having a strong desire for, to the point of greed.
Avid for the attention of their baby sitter, the children shouted and tumbled about on the floor.
2. Eager; enthusiastic.
Marcia is an **avid** skier who spends each weekend on the slopes.

brusque
brusk

adj. Abrupt in manner or speech; gruff.
The lawyer's **brusque** questioning intimidated the witness.
brusqueness *n.* The quality or state of being brusque.
With a **brusqueness** unlike her, Melanie ended the phone conversation.

concise
kən sīs´

adj. Short and to the point.
"Speed Kills" is a **concise** way of warning drivers of the danger of going too fast.

demean
dē mēn´

v. To cause a lowering of self-esteem; to lower in reputation or character.
Don't **demean** yourself by denying what everyone knows to be true.
demeaning *adj.* Degrading.
June felt that being scolded in front of her friends was **demeaning**.

despicable
des pik´ ə bəl

adj. Deserving contempt or scorn.
Stealing from the class treasury was a **despicable** thing to do.

emulate
em´ yōō lāt

v. To try to equal; to imitate.
Musicians around the world have tried to **emulate** Louis Armstrong's soulful trumpet playing.

evoke
ē vōk´

v. 1. To call forth; to produce.
After the oil spill, the governor's appeal for clean-up volunteers **evoked** a huge response from people in the state.
2. To bring to mind, often by suggestion.
The tinkling notes from the music box **evoked** for me the carefree joys of childhood.
evocative *adj.* (ē väk´ ə tiv) Creating something again, especially through the imagination.
The costumes and music of the film were **evocative** of Paris in the 1920s.

excruciating
eks krōō´ shē āt iŋ

adj. Very painful.
The ointment soothed the **excruciating** burn on Ronald's arm.

inaugurate
in ô´ gyər āt

v. 1. To install in office with a formal ceremony.
Presidents of the United States are **inaugurated** in January following the November election.
2. To begin officially or mark the opening of.
On Tuesday, Mayor Ovalles **inaugurated** a free vaccination program for all children under five living in the city.
inauguration *n.* The act of installing in office.
Governor Maitland was at her desk within hours of her **inauguration**.

pervade
pər vād´

v. To spread throughout.
Laughter **pervades** the house whenever Aunt Sara visits us.
pervasive *adj.* Spreading throughout.
Every Friday afternoon, the **pervasive** odor of disinfectant fills the halls as the cleaning crew mops the floors.

proprietor
prə prī´ ə tər

n. An owner of a store or other business.
The **proprietors** of the downtown shops planned a sidewalk sale for the first weekend in June.

pseudonym
soo´ də nim

n. A fictitious name used by an author; a pen name.
Female British authors of the nineteenth century often had to use a male **pseudonym** in order to get their books published.

rebuff
rē buf´

v. 1. To reject bluntly.
The owners **rebuffed** all attempts to take over their successful computer company.
2. To drive back.
Although the men in the Alamo were determined to **rebuff** Santa Anna's forces, in the end they were defeated.
n. 1. A blunt rejection.
Caroline's offer to Fred to patch up their quarrel met with a **rebuff**.
2. An abrupt setback in progress.
After a storm delayed their start, the climbers experienced another **rebuff** when a rock slide shut down one of the trails.

resilient
rē zil´ yənt

adj. 1. Capable of recovering quickly from misfortune.
After slipping to third place, the Red Sox were **resilient** enough to regain first place.
2. Returning quickly to an original shape or condition.
A wool sweater is more **resilient** after washing than a cotton one.
resilience *n.* 1. The ability to recover.
Steven's body showed great **resilience** after the chemotherapy treatment.
2. The ability to spring back.
Tennis balls lose **resilience** after three or four sets of vigorous play.

turbulent
tur´ byə lənt

adj. 1. Chaotic; unruly.
My brother and I tried our best to stay calm during the **turbulent** period of our parents' divorce.
2. Stormy; tempestuous.
Such a **turbulent** sea prevented all boats from leaving the harbor.
turbulence *n.* 1. Great disturbance or agitation.
The **turbulence** of the 1960s included peace marches, civil rights protests, and assassinations.
2. Rapid changes in wind speed and direction in the atmosphere.
The "Fasten Your Seatbelts" sign flashed on when the plane encountered **turbulence**.

1A Finding Meanings

Choose two phrases to form a sentence that correctly uses a word from Word List 1. Write each sentence in the space provided.

1. (a) To inaugurate someone is to
   (b) try to win that person's favor.

   (c) To rebuff someone is to
   (d) install that person in office.

2. (a) be unreliable or untrustworthy.   (c) To be avid is to
   (b) have a strong desire for something.   (d) To be resilient is to

3. (a) is to summon it from memory.   (c) To pervade something
   (b) To emulate something   (d) is to spread throughout it.

4. (a) one that is ignored.   (c) A despicable comment is
   (b) one that deserves contempt.   (d) A brusque comment is

5. (a) returns to its original shape.   (c) Something that is evocative
   (b) Something that is resilient   (d) is easily damaged.

6. (a) one that is favorable.   (c) A brusque remark is
   (b) one that is abrupt in manner.   (d) A concise remark is

7. (a) A proprietor is   (c) a story made up on the spur of the moment.
   (b) a fictitious name.   (d) A pseudonym is

8. (a) try to imitate that person.   (c) To emulate someone is to
   (b) try to influence that person.   (d) To demean someone is to

9. (a) An evocative poem   (c) is one that is difficult to understand.
   (b) A concise poem   (d) has the ability to bring back feelings.

10. (a) To demean someone is to   (c) reject that person.
    (b) To rebuff someone is to   (d) praise that person.

1B Just the Right Word

Improve each of the following sentences by crossing out the bold phrase and replacing it with a word (or a form of the word) from Word List 1.

1. The swelling in Denise's ankle was **so painful that she could hardly stand it**.

   excruciating

2. From Ms. Hernandez's **abrupt manner**, the students understood immediately that something was wrong. *brusque*

3. The 1930s was a **very disturbed and agitated** decade in European history.

   turbulent

4. When the lawyer attempted to **harm the reputation of** the witness by calling her a liar, the judge intervened. *demean*

5. Who is the **person with the legal right to the ownership** of the furniture business?

   proprietor

6. Without any explanation, Emi **bluntly rejected** Brandon's offer to help change the tire.

   rebuffed

7. Uncle Joshua used to be an **eager and enthusiastic** fan of the Cleveland Browns until they decided to move to Baltimore. *avid*

8. A worker needs to be **able to recover quickly from misfortune** in order to survive in these difficult times. *resilient*

9. The **installation into office** of Ruth Bader Ginsburg as a justice of the Supreme Court occurred in 1993. *inauguration*

10. Ernest Hemingway wrote in a style that was **short and to the point**.

    concise

avid
brusque
concise
demean
despicable
emulate
evoke
excruciating
inaugurate
pervade
proprietor
pseudonym
rebuff
resilient
turbulent

1C Applying Meanings

Circle the letter of each correct answer to the questions below. Questions may have more than one correct answer.

1. Which of the following might employ a **pseudonym**?
   - (a) a writer
   - (b) a singer
   - (c) a president of a country
   - (d) a small business

2. Which of the following can have a **proprietor**?
   - (a) a corner store
   - (b) a small child
   - (c) a small business
   - (d) a government agency

3. Which of the following has **resilience**?
   - (a) a person
   - (b) a doormat
   - (c) a lawn
   - (d) a question

4. Which of the following can be **pervasive**?

    (a) time   ✓ (c) fear

    ✓ (b) silence   (d) a smell

5. Which of the following can be **inaugurated**?

    ✓ (a) a president   (c) a bad habit

    ✓ (b) a delivery service   ✓ (d) a promise

6. Which of the following can be **evoked**?

    (a) a loose tooth   ✓ (c) a happy memory

    ✓ (b) a grudging response   (d) a broken ski pole

7. Which of the following might suffer a **rebuff**?   *setback*

    ✓ (a) an announcement   ✓ (c) a proposal

    ✓ (b) an attack   (d) a neighbor

8. In which of the following might there be **turbulence**?

    (a) a relationship   ✓ (c) the ocean

    (b) the air   (d) a lawn

1D Word Study

Choose from the two words provided and use each word just once when filling in the spaces. One space should be left blank.

brusque / abrupt

1. I was greeted with a(n) _____ "no" when I asked if I could help.

2. A(n) _____ person seems always to be in a hurry.

3. The bus came to a(n) _____ stop when a dog ran directly in front of it.

rebuff / reject

4. If you like, you can _____ a card and take another from the top of the deck.

5. The soldiers were able to ____*rebuff*____ repeated charges by the enemy.

6. The agency will ____*reject*____ applications that are not properly signed and dated.

driveback = push back

emulate / imitate

7. To walk on the moon is a feat that no one is likely to ____*emulate*____ any time soon.

8. To _____ someone else's answers during a test can get a student in serious trouble.

9. To ____*imitate*____ the sound of bird calls is quite an accomplishment.

demeaning / despicable

10. There is nothing _demeaning_ about asking for help if you need it.

11. There was a _____ expression on his face as he warned us of the danger.

12. It is _despicable_ to buy a puppy and mistreat it.

turbulent / stormy

13. Everyone screamed as the _turbulent_ rapids almost overturned the raft.

14. The principal's voice grew _____ as he spoke of his concern for the school's future.

15. The forecast of _stormy_ weather caused the cancellation of all ferry crossings.

1E Passage

Read the passage below; then complete the exercise that follows.

A Poet of the People

Maya Angelou was honored by William Jefferson Clinton when he invited her to read a poem she had written to celebrate his **inauguration** as the forty-second president of the United States. This was a fitting tribute to the woman whose early life had seemed so empty of promise when she was born Marguerite Johnson in St. Louis, Missouri, sixty-four years before. she sums up that life **concisely** in these lines from one of her poems: ". . . birthing is hard / and dying is mean / and living's a trial in between."

When she was still a small child, her parents divorced; she and her older brother Bailey were raised by their grandmother, Annie Henderson, affectionately known as Momma. Mrs. Henderson was the **proprietor** of the only general store in Stamps, Arkansas, owned by an African-American. In her first book, *I Know Why the Caged Bird Sings,* Angelou **evokes** Momma's powerful presence as she lovingly describes the way her grandmother coped with the bigotry and racial hatred that was widespread in the country in the 1930s. It was this **resilience** that most impressed Angelou and which she herself tried to **emulate** throughout her life.

One example of such bigotry involved a visit to the dentist. With Angelou suffering from an **excruciating** toothache, Momma had no choice but to take her granddaughter to the town's only dentist, who was white. When she asked him to treat the little girl's toothache, he **rebuffed** her, using extremely **demeaning** language. He told her that he would rather put his hand in a dog's mouth than treat a black person. Momma reminded him that she had helped him in the past by making him interest-free loans; now she was asking a favor in return. But he **brusquely** asserted that his debts had been paid and ordered her to leave. After taking her grandchild out of the office, Momma returned and stood her ground. She demanded that the dentist pay her a fair rate of interest on the loans she had made him. Finally, he handed over ten dollars, a large sum in those days, and only then did she depart, her dignity intact. She traveled over thirty miles with her granddaughter to Texarkana, where the nearest African-American dentist practiced.

When Angelou was eight years old, she and her brother went to live with their mother in St. Louis. There her mother's boyfriend abused her and threatened to harm Bailey if she told anyone. When Angelou became ill, her mother discovered the **despicable** abuse. The boyfriend was brought to trial and convicted. But the shock of the experience left Angelou unable to speak for a year.

avid
brusque
concise
demean
despicable
emulate
evoke
excruciating
inaugurate
pervade
proprietor
pseudonym
rebuff
resilient
turbulent

In spite of her troubled and **turbulent** childhood, a spirit of optimism **pervades** *I Know Why the Caged Bird Sings*. In it, Angelou pays tribute to those who helped and encouraged her, among them a neighbor named Bertha Flowers, who gave her books and introduced her to the pleasures of reading poetry, drama, and great novels. As a result of Flowers's influence, Angelou became an **avid** reader. This led later to her dream of becoming a writer. Four more volumes of autobiography and many collections of poetry followed *I Know Why the Caged Bird Sings*. All appeared under her **pseudonym**, Maya Angelou, a name she began using in the 1950s.

It was a long and difficult road that she had traveled, but it led to the presidential platform where she read her poem "On the Pulse of Morning" to an audience of millions on that cold January day. Angelou had triumphed over many difficulties, strengthened by the deep faith expressed in these lines from the poem, "Lift up your hearts / Each new hour holds new chances / For a new beginning."

Answer each of the following questions in the form of a sentence. If a question does not contain a vocabulary word from this lesson's word list, use one in your answer. Use each word only once. Questions and answers will then contain all fifteen words (or forms of the words).

1. Why is it inaccurate to say that Momma was Mrs. Henderson's **pseudonym**?

2. Why would you not use the word **concise** to describe the title of Angelou's first book?

3. Why did Angelou compose "On the Pulse of Morning"?

4. Why did Mrs. Henderson have to be knowledgeable about business?

She is the proprietor of the only general store in Stamp

5. Why was Momma desperate to get her granddaughter to a dentist?

Her granddaughter had excruciating toothache.

6. How did the dentist let Momma know that she was not welcome?

He rebuffed her with demeaning language.

7. Why is Angelou's mother's boyfriend someone one would not **emulate**?

He was abusive and should not be emulate.

8. In what way did the dentist show **despicable** behavior?

9. What is the meaning of **evoke** as it is used in the passage?

Evoke means to call forth

10. What is one way that Angelou showed **resilience** in her life?

11. What is one example from the passage of Angelou's **turbulent** childhood?

12. What details in the passage suggest that Bertha Flowers's treatment of Angelou was not **brusque**?

13. In the 1930s, why is it likely that most African Americans experienced racial bigotry?

14. How do you know that Angelou did not **rebuff** President Clinton's request for a poem?

15. What is the meaning of **avid** as it is used in the passage?

FUN & FASCINATING FACTS

The original meaning of the verb **demean**, "to conduct oneself," suggested neither good nor bad behavior. (Jane's young cousins *demeaned* themselves in a proper manner during their stay with her.) Even though this meaning continues, a second meaning, "to act in a way that lowers one's reputation or character," has largely replaced it. (You *demean* yourself by asking favors of someone who has treated you so badly.)

The original meaning of the verb survives in *demeanor*, the noun form, which means "the manner in which one behaves or conducts oneself." (No one could tell from Bill's *demeanor* that he was very angry.)

People sentenced to death in Roman times were often crucified, a form of execution in which the hands and feet of the victim were nailed to a cross until death occurred, usually after a long time. Since the pain suffered by those executed in this way must have been extreme, it is easy to see how **excruciating** came to mean "very painful" or "agonizing." The word is formed from the Latin *crux*, which means "a cross."

Pseudonym, a false name used by writers and others in place of their real name, is formed from the Greek roots *pseudo*, "false," and *onuma*, "name."

Lesson 2

Word List
Study the definitions of the words below; then do the exercises for the lesson.

abrasion
ə brā´ zhən

n. 1. A wearing away or rubbing away by friction.
This protective coating helps to prevent **abrasion** of the floor tiles.
2. A scraped or worn area.
Natalie's fall during the basketball game resulted in an **abrasion** on her knee.
abrasive *adj.* 1. Causing wear by rubbing.
Don't use this **abrasive** cleaner on the vinyl bathtub because it will scratch the surface.
2. Harsh or rough in manner; irritating.
The bus driver's **abrasive** tone made the excited children settle down in their seats.

clad
klad

adj. Clothed or covered.
Clad in a black rubber suit, the diver jumped from the side of the rescue boat.

corroborate
kə räb´ ə rāt

v. To provide evidence to make more certain; to confirm.
Because he was standing at the stoplight when the accident occurred, Harry could **corroborate** the driver's statement.

cursory
kʉr´ sə rē

adj. Done in a hurry and with little attention to detail.
Sherlock Holmes made a **cursory** search of the bedroom before going into the dining room to question the family.

dehydrate
dē hī´ drāt

v. 1. To remove the water from.
The processing plant **dehydrates** vegetables that are used in the popular soups sold in our grocery store.
2. To become dry; to lose water from.
During a marathon, runners will **dehydrate** unless they drink the water offered them along the route.
dehydration *n.* The state of being dehydrated.
Dehydration from the drought has caused the plants to wilt.

derive
di rīv´

v. 1. To take or receive from a source.
After practicing so diligently, Hugh **derived** great satisfaction from the enthusiastic applause following his performance.
2. To obtain through reasoning.
We **derived** the answer to the question by applying Ohm's law.

electrify
ē lek´ trə fī

v. 1. To wire or equip with electric power.
We no longer used oil lamps in our summer cottage once it had been **electrified.**
2. To thrill or shock.
Brian Boitano's performance, which included a layback spin and several perfectly executed triple axels, **electrified** the audience.

endeavor
en dev´ ər

v. To attempt earnestly.
The person we spoke to at the embassy said she would **endeavor** to find the papers we needed.
n. A serious, earnest effort toward a goal.
Arthur's **endeavor** to score twenty points a game throughout the season was a success.

gingerly
jin´ jər lē

adj. Cautious; very careful.
Mr. Wu made a **gingerly** attempt to bring the disputing parties together.
adv. With extreme care or concern.
Ella ran her tongue **gingerly** over where her wisdom tooth had been extracted and winced.

grimace
grim´ əs

v. To make a face expressing feelings of pain, disgust, or contempt.
While the doctor described the series of painful tests she would need, Cheryl **grimaced** only once.
n. A facial expression that seems to express pain, contempt, or disgust.
A **grimace** crossed her face as she watched the old film clips showing the destruction of Sarajevo.

gruesome
grōō´ səm

adj. Causing shock or horror.
The book told the **gruesome** details of living in Europe during the time of the Black Plague.

inventory
in´ vən tôr ē

n. 1. A list of possessions or goods on hand.
Before we could get renters' insurance, we had to make an **inventory** of everything of value in the apartment.
2. The stock of goods on hand.
The store's **inventory** of sheets and blankets was very low after the winter sale.
v. To make a complete list of.
At least once a year, the pharmacist **inventories** the stock.

simulate
sim´ yōō lāt

v. 1. To take on the qualities of another; to imitate.
AstroTurf **simulates** real grass.
2. To pretend.
Although Iago **simulated** concern for Othello, he was carefully planning his destruction.
simulated *adj.* Made to look genuine while being artificial.
Simulated leather looks and feels like the real thing.
simulation *n.* An imitation of a possible situation.
The **simulation** of a natural gas explosion gave the local emergency crews a chance to practice rescue procedures.

succumb
sə kum´

v. 1. To give up or give in to; to yield.
After twenty-four hours on their feet, the relief workers **succumbed** to exhaustion, falling soundly to sleep on their cots.
2. To cease to exist; to die.
Smallpox was so pervasive in the eighteenth century that many people **succumbed.**

surmise
sər mīz´

v. To suppose something without sufficient evidence.
Heloise **surmised** that her visitors were late because of the traffic from the airport.
n. A guess.
My **surmise** is that the thief had been watching our house for weeks before breaking in.

2A Finding Meanings

Choose two phrases to form a sentence that correctly uses a word from Word List 2. Write each sentence in the space provided.

1. (a) To surmise something
   (b) To electrify something
   (c) is to put it to death.
   (d) is to suppose it to be true.

2. (a) is to be covered.
   (b) To be dehydrated
   (c) is to feel faint from hunger.
   (d) To be clad

3. (a) a change in attitude.
   (b) An abrasion is
   (c) a wearing away of the surface.
   (d) A grimace is

4. (a) supply it with electric power.
   (b) prove it didn't take place.
   (c) To derive something is to
   (d) To electrify something is to

5. (a) a facial expression of dislike.
   (b) A grimace is
   (c) An endeavor is
   (d) a failure to do what is required.

6. (a) cause it to become active.
   (b) To dehydrate something is to
   (c) remove the water from it.
   (d) To simulate something is to

7. (a) an earnest attempt.
   (b) An endeavor is
   (c) An inventory is
   (d) an educated guess.

8. (a) is to recover from it.
   (b) is to imitate it.
   (c) To simulate something
   (d) To corroborate something

9. (a) To inventory something
   (b) To succumb to something
   (c) is to carefully avoid it.
   (d) is to give in to it.

10. (a) To corroborate something
   (b) is to end it abruptly.
   (c) is to obtain it through reasoning.
   (d) To derive something

2B Just the Right Word

Improve each of the following sentences by crossing out the bold phrase and replacing it with a word (or a form of the word) from Word List 2.

1. Your friend has **told us things that lead us to believe** your story.

2. The newspaper photographs of the automobile accident were **shocking and horrible.**

3. Although I planned to avoid dessert, when the waitress showed me the chocolate mousse, I **gave in** to my desire for sweets.

4. Katia will **make a serious effort** to improve her score on the next biology test.

5. Mario's running shoes were just a little too tight, so that after the race he had **scraped areas** on his heel.

6. Griswold's Hardware Store carries a complete **stock of everything** for painting your house.

7. Monica **made a face expressing disgust** when she learned she had to work the holiday weekend.

8. Many American legal principles **were taken** from English common law.

9. The German border guard searched the car in a **hurried and inattentive** manner before waving us through the checkpoint.

10. Detective Jones lifted the knife **with extreme care** from the desk drawer.

abrasion

clad

corroborate

cursory

dehydrate

derive

electrify

endeavor

gingerly

grimace

gruesome

inventory

simulate

succumb

surmise

2C Applying Meanings

Circle the letter of each correct answer to the questions below. Questions may have more than one correct answer.

1. Which of the following can be **simulated**?
   - (a) fur
   - (b) surprise
   - (c) anger
   - (d) sleep

2. Which of the following can be **abrasive**?
   - (a) a bright light
   - (b) a bad headache
   - (c) a surface
   - (d) a person's manner

3. Which of the following can be **dehydrated**?

    (a) food   (c) steam

    (b) water   (d) milk

4. Which of the following might be included in an **inventory**?

    (a) grocery items   (c) parts of a country

    (b) articles of clothing   (d) parts of an automobile

5. Which of the following can be **cursory**?

    (a) a search   (c) a smile

    (b) a discovery   (d) an examination

6. Which of the following might need to be **corroborated**?

    (a) an explanation   (c) an account

    (b) an accusation   (d) a joke

7. Which of the following should be done **gingerly**?

    (a) chewing on a new filling   (c) handling fragile papers

    (b) disarming a bomb   (d) running a 100-meter race

8. Which of the following can be **clad**?

    (a) Arctic explorers   (c) house plants

    (b) horses   (d) swimsuits

2D Word Study

In each group below, circle the two words that are synonyms.

1. copy	emulate	adjust	rebuff
2. avid	cursory	stormy	turbulent
3. succumb	grimace	increase	die
4. electrify	reject	evoke	rebuff
5. attempt	endeavor	derive	decide

In each group below, circle the two words that are antonyms.

6. brusque	gentle	resilient	gruesome
7. simulate	demand	praise	demean
8. admirable	despicable	turbulent	pervasive
9. rebuff	pervade	surmise	welcome
10. concise	cursory	calm	turbulent

ZE Passage

Read the passage below; then complete the exercise that follows.

The Iceman

On September 19, 1991, a German couple, returning from a day of hiking in the ten-thousand-foot high Otztaler region of the Alps made a **gruesome** discovery. The head and shoulders of a body protruded from the glacial ice in a shallow trench in the rock. With the nose and upper lip twisted up to the side, the face was set in a terrible **grimace**. Believing that they had discovered some unfortunate hiker, the couple reported their find at the mountain lodge where they were spending the night.

The first **endeavors** by mountain rescuers to free the body were unsuccessful because the location was remote and winter weather was beginning. A day or two later, the police asked medical experts from Innsbruck to assist in the recovery. Flying by helicopter to the site, they proceeded in a **gingerly** manner to chip away the ice until the body was free. Quickly placing it in a plastic body bag, they had it transported to Innsbruck for examination.

There it was stored in a freezer that **simulated** the conditions on the mountain. At the same time, an **inventory** of the objects found with or near the body was taken. Because some of these items appeared to be at least a hundred years old and to have historical significance, scientists at the University of Innsbruck were consulted. When they estimated that the find was 4,000 years old, everyone was astounded. Further tests established that the remains were actually 5,200 years old, an age later **corroborated** by tests at several independent institutions.

Scientists were **electrified** by the discovery. Not only would they be able to study the man's body, but also they would be able to **derive** information from his clothing and equipment about the age in which he had lived, the Late Neolithic period or Late Stone Age. A **cursory** examination of the body showed it to be in a remarkable state of preservation. Scientists believed that soon after the man **succumbed** to the cold, his body was **dehydrated** by the dry, icy winds of the high Alps. Subsequently, it was buried in snow, which filled the trench. As time passed this turned into packed ice, sealing the body and protecting it from harmful exposure to the air.

Further investigation revealed several interesting details. From the **abrasion** of his front teeth and the wear on his joints, scientists estimated the man's age at death to have been somewhere between thirty and forty years. His height was just over five feet. He had been **clad** in neatly sewn deerskin garments, with a grass cape to keep out the cold. With him were an ax with a long wooden handle, an unfinished bow and a leather quiver filled with arrows, a small leather pouch containing a flint scraper and some arrow tips, and a small knife.

At first, scientists were puzzled by several tattoos on the man's body—a blue cross on the back of one knee and a number of small parallel lines grouped together on his back and ankles. But when examinations showed that in each of these places the man's joints and bones showed wear or injury, they **surmised** that the markings may have been associated with some kind of primitive medical treatment.

In March, 2003, Eduard Egarter Vigl, official caretaker of the 5,300-year-old mummy at the Archaeological Museum in Bolzano, Italy, announced that he had found a deep knife wound on the mummy's right hand. "It is a severe, painful wound, certainly caused during a struggle," Vigl said. He believes the man died following a violent encounter with one or more people. The startling announcement followed the discovery a year earlier of an arrowhead wound in the man's left shoulder.

The exact details of what happened on that day more than 5,000 years ago will never be known. However, the Iceman has provided us with a revealing glimpse of life in the Late Stone

abrasion

clad

corroborate

cursory

dehydrate

derive

electrify

endeavor

gingerly

grimace

gruesome

inventory

simulate

succumb

surmise

Age. Both his well-preserved body and the clothing and tools that were with him are unique remains of a time before writing or cities had come into existence.

Answer each of the following questions in the form of a sentence. If a question does not contain a vocabulary word from this lesson's word list, use one in your answer. Use each word only once. Questions and answers will then contain all fifteen words (or forms of the words).

1. How do we know that the Iceman had been prepared for cold weather?

2. What is the meaning of **succumb** as it is used in the passage?

3. What did the German climbers **surmise** about their discovery?

4. What kind of **abrasion** did scientists examine on the Iceman?

5. Would you describe this story of the Iceman as **gruesome**? Explain your answer.

6. Why was it necessary to remove the body from the ice in a **gingerly** manner?

7. Why do you think it was important to place the body in conditions that **simulated** those on the mountain?

8. From the **inventory** of items found with his body, what conclusions would you draw about the Iceman's life?

9. What is one thing the scientists learned about the Iceman that could not be determined by a **cursory** examination?

10. How can we be certain that the body was 5,200 years old?

11. Why do you think the Iceman's face looked as it did?

12. How did weather conditions in the Alps preserve the body?

13. What was the first step after the body was discovered?

14. What information could the scientists **derive** from the amount of wear on the Iceman's teeth?

15. Why would it be inaccurate to say that scientists were not interested in the Iceman?

FUN & FASCINATING FACTS

The prefix *de-* has a number of meanings, including "to remove." To *dehorn* cattle is to remove their horns; to *dethrone* a monarch is to remove that person from the throne. This prefix is combined with the Greek root *hydro,* "water," to form the verb **dehydrate**. To *dehydrate* something is to remove the water from it. Other words formed from this Greek root include: *hydrogen,* "a gas that combines with oxygen to form water"; *hydrant,* "a closed pipe at a street curb with a spout from which water can be drawn to fight fires"; and *hydraulics,* "the science of the behavior of liquids, as water, at rest, or in motion."

An adjective is normally changed into an adverb by adding the *-ly* suffix; a *slow* driver is someone who drives *slowly*. But what if the adjective itself ends in *-ly,* as is the case with **gingerly**? Faced with writing *gingerlyly* as the adverbial form, users of the English language wisely decided that the adjective and adverb forms would be the same.

Simulate means "to imitate." (An animal will sometimes prevent an attack by *simulating* death.) Don't confuse this word with *stimulate,* which means "to make active." (Light *stimulates* growth in plants.) A word related to *simulate* is *dissimulate,* which means "to hide one's true feelings" or "to put up a false appearance." (The judge's penetrating questions made it very difficult for the witness to *dissimulate*.)

Lesson 3

> **Word List** — Study the definitions of the words below; then do the exercises for the lesson.

anonymous
ə nän´ ə məs

adj. Of an unknown source or unrevealed name.
It is frustrating to be unable to thank the person who gave this **anonymous** donation to our library fund.

anthology
an thäl´ ə jē

n. A collection of various writings, such as songs, stories, or poems.
This **anthology** of science-fiction stories includes some by Ray Bradbury, Julian May, and Ursula Le Guin.

conjecture
kən jek´ chər

n. A conclusion based on guesswork or insufficient evidence.
Dad's **conjecture** that the derelict building would be a problem proved to be correct when it caught on fire.
v. To form an opinion while lacking sufficient evidence.
The fire chief **conjectured** that oily rags may have been the cause of the fire.

disposition
dis pə zish´ ən

n. 1. A person's usual mood; temperament.
People enjoy Alice's company because of her sunny **disposition**.
2. A regular tendency or inclination.
Roberto's **disposition** to argue about everything can sometimes get him into trouble.

encompass
en kum´ pəs

v. 1. To enclose or encircle.
Except for one narrow pass, mountains **encompass** the village of Neudorf on all sides.
2. To include.
This year's report on available housing **encompasses** the results of seventy-five surveys.

extricate
eks´ tri kāt

v. To free from a difficult or tangled situation.
Extricating our bags from the bus's crowded storage area was much simpler than we thought it would be.

generation
jen ər ā´ shən

n. 1. One step in the line of descent of a family.
Four **generations** were represented at Norma's family reunion last summer.
2. All the people born and living about the same time.
My father's **generation** lived through the Civil Rights Movement and the Vietnam War.
3. The average span of time between the birth of parents and their children.
Within one **generation** this town became a city.

guile
gīl

n. Cunning or deceit in dealing with others; trickery.
The Grimm brothers vividly described the wolf's **guile** toward Little Red Riding Hood.

imperative
im per´ ə tiv

adj. 1. Urgent; pressing.
The lawyer made us understand why it is **imperative** that we find the missing papers before tomorrow.
2. Having the power or authority to command.
Because of the **imperative** tone of the letter, Ida began immediately to search for the facts she needed for a reply.

instill *or* **instil**
in stil´

v. To introduce gradually in order to establish securely.
Juanita's love of animals was **instilled** during the summer vacations spent at her uncle's farm as a child.

modify
mäd´ ə fī

v. 1. To make less extreme or severe.
Congress may **modify** some portions of the welfare reform law they just approved.
2. To make changes in.
The teenagers **modified** their language when they tutored young children after school.
3. In grammar, to limit or restrict in meaning.
Most of us know that in the phrase "the black chair," the adjective "black" **modifies** the noun "chair."

pivot
piv´ ət

n. 1. A small bar or rod on which something else turns.
The gate swung shut easily on its well-oiled **pivot**.
2. A person or thing on which others depend.
The quarterback is the **pivot** of a team's offense.
v. To turn on or as if on a pivot.
A weathervane **pivots** when the wind changes direction.
pivotal *adj.* Vitally important; significant.
The first human landing on Mars will be a **pivotal** event in the history of space exploration.

prevalent
prev´ ə lənt

adj. Commonly occurring; widely accepted or practiced.
Both chicken pox and the flu were **prevalent** in the Edison Middle School last winter.

recur
rē kur´

v. 1. To come up again or to happen again.
Throughout Mozart's *The Magic Flute*, certain musical themes **recur** each time a particular character appears on stage.
2. To come to mind again.
The events on the night of the robbery **recurred** to Hank several times in the following weeks.
recurrence *n.* The act of recurring.
Engineers hope that the new dam will prevent a **recurrence** of flooding.

spontaneous
spän tā´ nē əs

adj. 1. Voluntary and unplanned.
The crowd burst into a **spontaneous** chant of "Go! Go! Go!" as the first two runners neared the finish line.
2. Occurring or produced without human labor.
The **spontaneous** growth on the forest floor provided a habitat for a great number of creatures.
spontaneity *n.* (spän tə nā´ ə tē) The quality or condition of occurring in an unplanned way.
With an unexpected **spontaneity**, Isabelle rose to embrace her friend.

anonymous
anthology
conjecture
disposition
encompass
extricate
generation
guile
imperative
instill *or* instil
modify
pivot
prevalent
recur
spontaneous

3A Finding Meanings

Choose two phrases to form a sentence that correctly uses a word from Word List 3. Write each sentence in the space provided.

1. (a) be commonly accepted.
   (b) To be pivotal is to
   (c) To be prevalent is to
   (d) occur without a known cause.

2. (a) Guile is
   (b) Conjecture is
   (c) a failure to take proper precautions.
   (d) cunning or deceit in dealing with others.

3. (a) To modify something is to   (c) To extricate something is to
   (b) set it free.   (d) restore it to its proper place.

4. (a) A recurrence is   (c) a handwritten document.
   (b) An anthology is   (d) a collection of writings.

5. (a) An anonymous donation   (c) is one made without previous thought.
   (b) A spontaneous donation   (d) is one made with conditions attached.

6. (a) To instill something is to   (c) To modify something is to
   (b) bring it to an end.   (d) make changes to it.

7. (a) A recurring event is one   (c) that is of great importance.
   (b) A pivotal event is one   (d) that cannot be repeated.

8. (a) To encompass something is to   (c) To instill something is to
   (b) prevent it from occurring.   (d) enclose or encircle it.

9. (a) a carefully planned event.   (c) A conjecture is
   (b) a single step in a family's descendants. (d) A generation is

10. (a) An anonymous statement   (c) An imperative statement
    (b) is one expressing authority.   (d) is one that is handwritten.

3B Just the Right Word

Improve each of the following sentences by crossing out the bold phrase and replacing it with a word (or a form of the word) from Word List 3.

1. Hercule Poirot refused to make a **judgment based on insufficient evidence** when asked about the time of the robbery.

2. As soon as Paul Revere knew how the British soldiers were approaching Boston, it was **extremely urgent** that he ride to Lexington with the information.

3. The author of the concise sixteenth-century poem "O Western Wind" is **someone whose name is not known.**

4. While you are at the library, will you look for this **collection of writings** of Bolivian authors?

5. Looking at the color and composition of the children's drawings, I was struck by their **unplanned and natural manner**.

6. At the Air Force Academy, the instructors try to **introduce gradually** a strong sense of duty in the minds of all cadets.

7. After having surgery to remove the tumor, my father received chemotherapy so that the cancer would not **happen again.**

8. Rafael has a **regular tendency** to do things in a careful, thorough manner.

9. This **group of people born at about the same time** was given the name "baby boomers."

10. The gigantic telescope was attached to a huge pin that allowed the machine to **turn freely in a circle.**

3C Applying Meanings

Circle the letter of each correct answer to the questions below. Questions may have more than one correct answer.

anonymous

anthology

conjecture

disposition

encompass

extricate

generation

guile

imperative

instill *or* instil

modify

pivot

prevalent

recur

spontaneous

1. Which of the following is expressed in an **imperative** manner?
   - (a) "Go to your room!"
   - (b) "Are you ready?"
   - (c) "Please turn down the volume."
   - (d) "Don't do that!"

2. Which of the following could have a **recurrence**?
   - (a) a toothache
   - (b) an illness
   - (c) a nightmare
   - (d) a child's first birthday

3. Which of the following could be **modified**?
   - (a) an adjective
   - (b) a building
   - (c) a plan
   - (d) time

4. Which of the following is a **generation**?
   - (a) a period of about twenty years
   - (b) all the people born around 1990
   - (c) the life span of a plant
   - (d) the members of your family

5. Which of the following might be included in an **anthology**?

  (a) a play   (c) a short story

  (b) a poem   (d) a three-volume biography

6. Which of the following could be **instilled**?

  (a) manners   (c) values

  (b) punishment   (d) ideas

7. Which of the following could be **spontaneous**?

  (a) a nosebleed   (c) a decision

  (b) laughter   (d) an inventory

8. Which of the following could describe a person's **disposition**?

  (a) grouchy   (c) tall

  (b) pleasant   (d) handsome

3D Word Study

Each group of four words below contains two words that are either synonyms or antonyms. Circle these two words; then circle the *S* if they are synonyms, the *A* if they are antonyms.

1. instill	pivot	turn	recur	S	A
2. anonymous	imperative	unknown	avid	S	A
3. encompass	exclude	conjecture	praise	S	A
4. imperative	exact	urgent	cursory	S	A
5. prevalent	cheap	resilient	rare	S	A
6. spontaneous	pivotal	important	wealthy	S	A
7. guess	corroborate	rebuff	conjecture	S	A
8. modify	recover	recur	change	S	A
9. disposition	guile	innocence	endeavor	S	A
10. remove	extricate	encompass	rebuff	S	A

3E Passage

Read the passage below; then complete the exercise that follows.

Telling Tales

The invention of writing, more than 5,000 years ago, was a **pivotal** event in human history; indeed, without it there could be no recorded history. But even before writing began, stories existed, often in the form of folk tales. This much older spoken tradition probably goes back to the very beginnings of language itself. Folk tales did not need to be written in order to be preserved because they were passed on by word of mouth from one **generation** to the next. Most were **anonymous** and the work of many different people. As the tale was told and retold, it changed, each teller **modifying** it to fit a particular audience.

One famous collection of folk tales, first recorded around the fourteenth century, is *The Arabian Nights*, also called *One Thousand and One Nights*. The title comes from the efforts of the storyteller, Scheherazade, to keep her husband, the king of what is now India and Indochina, from killing her. She stopped each night's story at a suspenseful point so that her husband would allow her to live one more night to tell its ending. Scholars think that many of these tales may have originated in Syria and Egypt, while others could have come from India, but their actual origin remains a matter of **conjecture**.

Not until the early nineteenth century was a serious attempt made to give European folk tales a permanent written form. In Germany, two brothers, Jacob and Wilhelm Grimm, collected hundreds of folk tales from all parts of the country and published them in an **anthology**, now well known as *Grimm's Fairy Tales*. In its pages Rapunzel, Hansel and Gretel, Cinderella, and Little Red Riding Hood make their first appearance in print.

While one purpose of folk tales may have been to entertain, that was not their only function. The reason they have survived for so long and are so **prevalent** in all human societies is that they educate their audiences. They seek to **instill** values that the society may consider **imperative** for its survival, such as a sense of right and wrong or the need for self-reliance. In addition to providing models for appropriate behavior, they give explanations, often derived from folklore, of the origin and meaning of the natural world.

Scholars have been struck by how frequently the same situations **recur** in folk tales from many

anonymous
anthology
conjecture
disposition
encompass
extricate
generation
guile
imperative
instill *or* instil
modify
pivot
prevalent
recur
spontaneous

different places; over three hundred versions of the Cinderella story, for example, have been identified. Perhaps the same stories appeared **spontaneously** in many distant societies, or perhaps they were spread by travelers and adapted to fit the needs of their listeners. In addition to the same stories, the same themes are also found again and again. One of the commonest is the use of **guile** as a weapon of the helpless against the powerful. There are no better examples of this than the *Uncle Remus* stories of Joel Chandler Harris, based on African-American folk tales of the American South.

One of the funniest of the Uncle Remus stories tells of Brer Rabbit, who falls into the clutches of Brer Fox. He begs his captor not to throw him into the brier patch, saying he would rather be hanged, drowned, or even skinned alive. Brer Fox, being of a mean **disposition**, promptly does what his victim has begged him not to do. Brer Rabbit, of course, **extricates** himself with ease from the brier patch, mocking Brer Fox as he scampers away by calling out that he was "bred and born in a brier patch."

Folk tales, coming from every part of the globe, **encompass** the whole of human experience. From their early beginnings, long before the dawn of history, until the fairly recent past, they had no competition from other forms of entertainment. Today, worldwide television and radio, movies, and the mass marketing of books compete for children's attention. Is there a danger that in the future folk tales will survive only in scholarly collections? Probably not as long as children, snuggled in their beds, experience the magic that begins with the spoken words, "Once upon a time."

Answer each of the following questions in the form of a sentence. If a question does not contain a vocabulary word from this lesson's word list, use one in your answer. Use each word only once. Questions and answers will then contain all fifteen words (or forms of the words).

1. Why was it **imperative** that Scheherazade keep the king entertained?

2. What is the meaning of **generation** as it is used in the passage?

3. Why are the Grimm brothers **pivotal** figures in the history of folktales?

4. How would you describe the temperament of Scheherazade's husband?

5. Who first made up the stories of Cinderella and Little Red Riding Hood?

6. Why would it be inaccurate to say that Scheherazade's stories were **spontaneous**?

7. In which parts of the world do folk tales commonly occur?

8. What purpose do folk tales have besides being entertaining?

9. Why do you think folk tales using the theme of **guile** are so common?

10. Why did Brer Rabbit ask to be thrown into the brier patch?

11. Why do you think the same themes **recur** in folk tales from different countries?

12. What is *The Arabian Nights*?

13. What is the meaning of **encompass** as it is used in the passage?

14. In what way might a written folk tale differ from a spoken one?

15. What **conjecture** is made in the passage about the age of folk tales?

FUN & FASCINATING FACTS

A person who collects the best writings of different authors or poets and arranges them into an **anthology** could be compared to a person who gathers a variety of flowers and arranges them into a bouquet. If this comparison seems a little far-fetched, consider the origin of the word *anthology*. It comes from two Greek words, *anthos*, "flower," and *legein*, "to gather."

In addition to the definitions given in the word list, **imperative** has a grammatical meaning. It is the name for the mood of a verb used in giving orders or commands. In the sentence, "Stop him from crossing the street!", the verb *stop* is in the imperative mood.

William Shakespeare (1564–1616) is rightly regarded as one of the world's great writers; yet it would seem that he couldn't spell his own name! Samples of his signature that have survived show his name spelled in several different ways. Such variation, however, was common then with the spelling of many words, not just names. Not until the eighteenth century when dictionaries came into use was a single spelling for each word accepted as correct. A few words, however, escaped being standardized in this way; **instill** (which can also be spelled *instil*) is one of them. When a dictionary gives two different spellings of a word, the one given first is preferred.

Lesson 4

Word List Study the definitions of the words below; then do the exercises for the lesson.

abhor
ab hôr´

v. To shrink from in disgust; to detest. *dislike*
We **abhor** cruelty in all its forms.
abhorrent *adj.* Disgusting; causing loathing.
The caste system was **abhorrent** to Gandhi.

affable
af´ ə bəl

adj. Pleasant; approachable; gracious.
Maribel's **affable** manner brought her many friends.
affability *n.* Friendliness of manner.
The counselor welcomed the young campers with such **affability** that not one felt homesick.

amiss
ə mis´

adv. In a wrong or imperfect way.
Don't take **amiss** my suggestion for improving your drawing.
adj. Out of order; wrong. *improperly*
Although the door to the school was wide open when we arrived at 7:30, nothing in the office seemed **amiss** at first.

despondent
də spän´ dənt

adj. Depressed from loss of hope or confidence; utterly discouraged.
Failing my driver's test for the third time left me completely **despondent**.

entreat
en trēt´

v. To ask earnestly; to beg.
"Please, please, let me have a dog," Augustin **entreated** his parents; "I promise to take care of it!"
entreaty *n.* A plea or earnest request.
The umpire ignored the manager's **entreaties** to reverse the call.

haunt
hônt

v. 1. To stay in one's mind continually.
Even though I saw *Platoon* over a week ago, the music continues to **haunt** me.
2. To visit frequently.
Ishmael **haunted** the waterfront, hoping to find a job on a whaling ship.
3. To appear in the form of a ghost.
The Headless Horseman **haunted** the hollow where Ichabod Crane rode his horse.

impel
im pel´

v. 1. To drive or to propel.
A raging current **impelled** their raft downstream toward the waterfall.
2. To urge or drive by force or moral pressure.
Hatred of slavery **impelled** Harriet Tubman to return repeatedly to the South to help other slaves escape.

interminable
in tur´ mi nə bəl

adj. Endless; seeming to be without end.
We had an **interminable** wait at the airport because the heavy snowstorm shut down the runways.

irascible
i ras´ ə bəl

adj. Quick-tempered; irritable.
My grandfather looked kindly, but he was really quite **irascible.**

profound
prō found´

adj. 1. Intense; deeply felt.
Parents who had been separated from their children at the beginning of the war felt **profound** joy when they were reunited in the refugee camp.
2. Having understanding or knowledge that goes beneath the surface, beyond the obvious.
Profound insights from Thoreau and Gandhi influenced Martin Luther King's ideas about non-violent protest.

recluse
rek´ lōōs

n. A person who lives apart from society and often alone.
Jamie became a **recluse** when his wife died, refusing even to answer his mail.
reclusive *adj.* Withdrawn from society.
Our neighbors are so **reclusive** that we hardly see them from one year to the next.

reverberate
rē vur´ bər āt

v. To be repeated as in a series of echoes or vibrations.
We loved to hear our shouts **reverberate** as we ran through the old tunnel.

sage
sāj

adj. Having wisdom and good judgment.
Ben Franklin's Poor Richard's Almanack offered **sage** advice to the colonists.
n. 1. A person known for wisdom and good judgment.
When I need advice, I consult my grandmother, the family **sage**.
2. An aromatic grayish-green plant used in cooking.
Sage and onion are essential ingredients for a good turkey stuffing.

tirade
tī´ rād

n. A long, angry speech.
The British soldiers, tiring of the speaker's **tirade** about high taxes on tea, ordered the crowd to move along.

tremulous
trem´ yōō ləs

adj. 1. Marked by trembling or shaking.
Marie tried to look brave as the nurse prepared to give her an injection, but her **tremulous** lower lip betrayed her.
2. Timid or fearful.
In a **tremulous** voice, Alejandro began his first stage appearance as Prospero.

abhor
affable
amiss
despondent
entreat
haunt
impel
interminable
irascible
profound
recluse
reverberate
sage
tirade
tremulous

4A Finding Meanings

Choose two phrases to form a sentence that correctly uses a word from Word List 4. Write each sentence in the space provided.

1. (a) If something is interminable,
   (b) If something is amiss,
   (c) it changes frequently.
   (d) it is not right.

2. (a) have a vivid memory of it.
   (b) To haunt something is
   (c) To impel something is
   (d) to move it along.

3. (a) A profound answer is one   (c) that seems to have no end.
   (b) An interminable answer is one   (d) that makes a person laugh.

4. (a) An entreaty is   (c) a solemn agreement.
   (b) A recluse is   (d) an earnest request.

5. (a) is to spend time there repeatedly. (c) To abhor a place
   (b) is to have fond memories of it.   (d) To haunt a place

6. (a) a long, angry speech.   (c) an angry person.
   (b) A tirade is   (d) A sage is

7. (a) An affable remark   (c) is one that is made spontaneously.
   (b) is one that causes disgust.   (d) An abhorrent remark

8. (a) one that is intended to confuse.   (c) one that expresses deep understanding.
   (b) A profound statement is   (d) A despondent statement is

9. (a) An irascible person is one who   (c) is easy to get along with.
   (b) A reclusive person is one who   (d) is easily angered.

10. (a) Tremulous words   (c) are words that seem to make no sense.
    (b) Sage words   (d) are words spoken in fear.

4B Just the Right Word

Improve each of the following sentences by crossing out the bold phrase and replacing it with a word (or a form of the word) from Word List 4.

1. What on earth **was it that made** you to talk back to the principal?

2. Rachel **has a very strong dislike of** people who say one thing but do another.

3. Rumbling thunder **continued to echo** through the long narrow valley.

4. Born in China thousands of years ago, Lao-tzu is still considered a **person who possessed great wisdom.**

5. Tony's first pitch went **in an imperfect way,** almost striking the batter.

6. My sister was **feeling very discouraged** when she was unable to participate in the violin competition.

7. Frederick Douglass **earnestly begged** his audience to work to abolish slavery.

8. In order to think and write, Thoreau lived a **separate and solitary** life for two years at Walden Pond.

9. Juliet's voice was **shaking and unsteady** with grief as she begged the nurse to comfort her.

10. Garrison Keillor's **pleasant and gracious manner** has made him a popular radio host.

4C Applying Meanings

Circle the letter of each correct answer to the questions below. Questions may have more than one correct answer.

1. Which of the following might be said of **sage**?

   (a) It has an aroma.

   (b) It is used in cooking.

   (c) It is burned for fuel.

   (d) It is grayish green.

2. Which of the following might have a **reclusive** existence?

   (a) a politician

   (b) an entertainer

   (c) a hermit

   (d) a lighthouse keeper

3. Which of the following is true of a **tirade**?

   (a) It expresses anger.

   (b) It is concise.

   (c) It offers comfort.

   (d) It is humorous.

4. Which of the following can be **tremulous**?

   (a) hands

   (b) words

   (c) persons

   (d) books

5. Which of the following might **haunt** a person?

   (a) a song

   (b) a memory

   (c) a face

   (d) a poem

abhor
affable
amiss
despondent
entreat
haunt
impel
interminable
irascible
profound
recluse
reverberate
sage
tirade
tremulous

6. Which of the following might an **affable** person say?

   (a) "So nice to see you."   (c) "Leave me alone."

   (b) "What can I do to help?"   (d) "Get lost!"

7. Which of the following might be **profound**?

   (a) a book   (c) a thought

   (b) a snowflake   (d) a person

8. Which of the following might **reverberate**?

   (a) the beat of a drum   (c) a flash of lightning

   (b) the warmth of fire   (d) a crack of thunder

4D Word Study

Complete the analogies by selecting the pair of words whose relationship most resembles the relationship of the pair in capital letters. Circle the letter in front of the pair you choose.

1. SAGE : WISDOM ::

   (a) hunter : prey   (b) speaker : tirade

   (c) author : anthology   (d) acrobat : agility

2. CONCISE : LENGTHY ::

   (a) avid : eager   (c) abrupt : brusque

   (b) cursory : thorough   (d) alone : despondent

3. AFFABILITY : SMILE ::

   (a) pain : grimace   (c) turbulence : pseudonym

   (b) resilience : recovery   (d) abrasion : bruise

4. GUILE : HONESTY ::

   (a) name : pseudonym   (c) entreaty : mercy

   (b) sickness : health   (d) surmise : guess

5. ITEM : INVENTORY ::

   (a) recluse : society   (c) poem : anthology

   (b) pivot : weathervane   (d) attempt : endeavor

6. SCOLDING : TIRADE ::

   (a) sage : wisdom   (c) guess : conjecture

   (b) breeze : gale   (d) crime : punishment

7. ENCOMPASS : EXCLUDE ::
  (a) rebuff : reject
  (b) lower : demean
  (c) remove : extricate
  (d) corroborate : disprove

8. PREVALENT : RARE ::
  (a) brief : concise
  (b) pervasive : isolated
  (c) turbulent : unruly
  (d) affable : happy

9. ABHOR : ADMIRE ::
  (a) emulate : copy
  (b) rob : steal
  (c) fix : adjust
  (d) rebuff : welcome

10. SAD : DESPONDENT ::
  (a) glad : ecstatic
  (b) weeping : tearful
  (c) smiling : happy
  (d) cursory : thorough

4E Passage

Read the passage below; then complete the exercise that follows.

The Tiger's Whisker

This folk tale from Korea tells us how love can heal deep wounds, not quickly or easily, but with patience and courage.

Once Kim Soo-Nyung's life was filled with happiness. She and her husband, Liang-Po, one of the most **affable** of men, cultivated the fields of their small farm and raised three children with never an angry word spoken between them. But when war broke out, Liang-Po was forced to serve in the army even though he **abhorred** violence.

While he was away, Soo-Nyung and her three children worked hard to ensure the success of the farm. They took satisfaction in planting and harvesting, caring for the livestock, and keeping the farm buildings in good repair, all without outside help. The war, though, dragged on **interminably**; there were times when Soo-Nyung grew **despondent**, thinking she would never see Liang-Po again. But one day in the early spring, as she was drawing water from the well, she looked up to see him limping along the road toward the farm. Scarcely able to believe her eyes, Soo-Nyung rushed to greet him and welcome him home.

Her joy was short-lived, however, for it did not take long to see that something was **amiss**. There had been a **profound** change in Liang-Po. He, who always had been ready for a joke or a romp with his children, was now **irascible** and snapped at them without cause. He shut himself away like a **recluse**, responding to Soo-Nyung's pleas that he join her and the children for the evening meal with a stony silence. If she persisted, he would launch into a **tirade** that caused her to flee his presence. He took no interest in the farm, no pleasure in his family, and refused to talk about what troubled him. In time, Soo-Nyung, having lost patience with her husband, had no more dealings with him.

abhor
affable
amiss
despondent
entreat
haunt
impel
interminable
irascible
profound
recluse
reverberate
sage
tirade
tremulous

Liang-Po's mother, who lived in the next village, was distressed by her daughter-in-law's unhappiness. She persuaded Soo-Nyung to visit a local herbalist, a woman who was famous as much for her **sage** advice as for her herbal remedies. Soo-Nyung's sad story touched this woman's heart. "Your husband undoubtedly witnessed terrible scenes while in the army, for that is the nature of war," she told Soo-Nyung. "He is **haunted** by those memories. Fortunately there is a cure, but it requires a whisker plucked from a wild tiger. When you bring it to me, you shall have the remedy your husband needs."

In a **tremulous** voice, Soo-Nyung thanked the herbalist. The thought of facing a wild tiger filled her with dread, but she loved her husband and this **impelled** her to follow the herbalist's instructions. She made her way to the tiger's lair, where she was greeted with a terrifying roar that **reverberated** through the forest. She fled in a panic, convinced that the wild beast was about to tear her limb from limb. Still, she found the courage to return the next day, this time with a piece of red meat. After smelling it suspiciously, the tiger devoured the meat.

Day after day, Soo-Nyung returned with more meat until the tiger grew so accustomed to her that she was finally able to rub its head and tickle its throat without being afraid. At last there came a day when she found the courage to reach out and pluck one of its whiskers. The tiger drew back and growled, but it did not attack her. Triumphantly, Soo-Nyung returned to the herbalist with the tiger's whisker, **entreating** her to prepare the remedy she needed.

The wise herbalist replied that Soo-Nyung had already found the cure. "If you can win the trust of a savage tiger," she said, "surely you can find the patience to regain the affection of your husband, whose heart has been hardened by war."

Soo-Nyung thanked the herbalist for teaching her a valuable lesson. In time her patience was rewarded when Liang-Po was restored to his former self.

Answer each of the following questions in the form of a sentence. If a question does not contain a vocabulary word from this lesson's word list, use one in your answer. Use each word only once. Questions and answers will then contain all fifteen words (or forms of the words).

1. How do we know that the war kept Liang-Po from his family for a long time?.

2. Why would it be inaccurate to describe Liang-Po as **irascible** at the end of the story?

3. Why did Liang-Po's mother want to help?

4. What kind of reputation did the woman have to whom Soo-Nyung went for help?

5. What is the meaning of **amiss** as it is used in the passage?

6. On what occasions did Liang-Po break his silence following his return?

7. Why would Liang-Po's **reclusive** behavior be very hard for the family to deal with?

8. How do we know that Liang-Po probably got along with his neighbors before the war?

9. What was the outcome of Soo-Nyung's **entreaty** to the herbalist for help?

10. Why was it likely that the tiger's roar startled other animals?

11. Why might Liang-Po have had trouble sleeping after his return?

12. How do we know that farm work was not **abhorrent** to Soo-Nyung?

13. Who **impelled** Soo-Nyung to visit the herbalist?

14. What does Liang-Po's snapping at his children tell you of his disposition after the war?

15. What is the meaning of **tremulous** as it is used in the passage?

FUN & FASCINATING FACTS

The Latin word *ira,* meaning "anger," forms the root of several English words having related meanings. *Ire* is a synonym for "anger." (In a carefully worded letter to the editor, James expressed his *ire* over the plans to build a mall in the center of town.) *Irate* and **irascible** are synonyms for "angry." *Irate* suggests a single instance of becoming angry. (Karen became *irate* when she saw that someone had left the gate open to the horse pasture.) *Irascible* suggests a continuing inability to control one's anger.

Review for Lessons 1–4

Crossword Puzzle Solve the crossword puzzle below by studying the clues and filling in the answer boxes. Clues followed by a number are definitions of words in Lessons 1 through 4. The number gives the word list in which the answer to the clue appears.

Clues Across

1. Cunning; deceit (3)
6. A facial expression of pain or disgust (2)
7. Eager (1)
11. Seeming to go on forever (4)
12. Friendly (4)
14. A passage under land or water
16. A young boy
17. To call forth (1)
19. To happen again (3)
20. To free from a difficult situation (3)
22. To receive from a source (2)
23. Having wisdom (4)
24. A long, angry speech (4)

Clues Down

2. To introduce gradually (3)
3. Extremely painful (1)
4. To try to equal (1)
5. An abrupt setback (1)
7. A wearing away by friction (2)
8. To lower in self-esteem (1)
9. To pretend (2)
10. Something on which a thing turns (3)
13. An earnest request (4)
15. Opposite of *quiet*
18. Nine, ten, _____
21. Another word for *exam*
22. A home for a lion

Lesson 5

➤ **Word List** Study the definitions of the words below; then do the exercises for the lesson.

audacious
ô dā´ shəs

adj. 1. Willing to take risks; daring.
Their **audacious** escape plan involved a helicopter landing in the prison yard.
2. Showing disrespect or a lack of courtesy.
Judge Miller admonished the defense lawyer for her **audacious** remarks to the expert witness.
audacity *n.* (ô das´ ə tē) Willingness to take risks by showing excessive boldness.
Oliver Twist was the only boy with the **audacity** to ask for more food.

confiscate
kän´ fi skāt

v. To seize, by force if necessary; to take possession of.
The Miami police **confiscated** the stolen paintings they found stored in a closet of the mansion.

conscientious
kän shē en´ shəs

adj. 1. Thorough; careful.
Because of our **conscientious** preparations, the science fair was enjoyable and informative for everyone.
2. Honest; principled.
Several of the students made a **conscientious** effort to combat hunger by working with the food bank.

depict
dē pikt´

v. To give a picture of; to describe.
Patrick O'Brian's seafaring novels **depict** life aboard a navy sailing ship with great accuracy.

embark
em bärk´

v. 1. To go on board a ship or airplane at the start of a voyage.
Around nine o'clock, we **embarked** at Woods Hole for a day of whale watching.
2. To start out; to begin.
Larry Bird **embarked** on his professional basketball career after finishing college.

inkling
iŋk´ liŋ

n. A slight suspicion; a vague idea.
As she opened the door, Shala had no **inkling** that her friends were hidden in the darkened room, waiting to shout "Surprise!"

lackadaisical
lak ə dāv zi kəl

adj. Showing little spirit or enthusiasm.
When the students came after school to work on their reports, the librarian was quite **lackadaisical** about enforcing the no-talking rule.

mutiny
myōōt´ n ē

n. Deliberate refusal to obey orders given by those in command, especially by sailors.
The 1917 **mutiny** by French soldiers could have caused France to lose the war.
v. To rebel openly against a commander.
Captain Vere feared the sailors would **mutiny** if he didn't discipline Billy Budd.

pilfer
pil´ fər

v. To steal repeatedly small amounts or things that are of little value.
Pip **pilfered** bread and other bits of food from his sister's kitchen to feed the man in hiding.

profusion
prō fyōō´ zhən

n. A plentiful supply; a great or generous amount.
Daffodils grew in **profusion** along the river bank.
profuse *adj.* Given or occurring in generous amounts; abundant.
Jerry's **profuse** apologies convinced me he was sorry he had hurt my feelings.

| **prudent** prōōd´ nt | *adj.* Very careful; showing judgment and wisdom.
Lost in the forest, Amy argued it was more **prudent** to wait until morning to find the trail than to continue wandering in the dark.
prudence *n.* The avoidance of risk; carefulness in what one says or does.
Although the knight was shaking with anger, he exercised **prudence**, saying nothing to the king who had insulted him. |
|---|---|
| **rankle** raŋ´ kəl | *v.* To cause continuing anger or irritation.
The unfair criticism still **rankled** Deena, even though her friend later apologized. |
| **rebuke** rē byōōk´ | *v.* To criticize strongly; to reprimand.
We all watched as Mom **rebuked** Nina for running into the street without looking.
n. A sharp criticism.
My employer's **rebuke** seemed to include every mistake I had made since beginning the job. |
| **serene** sə rēn´ | *adj.* Calm and untroubled; peaceful.
The nurse's **serene** manner comforted the patients.
serenity *n.* (sə ren´ ə tē) A calm and untroubled state.
One way to achieve **serenity** is to practice yoga. |
| **slovenly** sluv´ ən lē | *adj.* Untidy; carelessly done.
Because of the carpenter's **slovenly** measuring, the floor was one inch higher at the back of the room than at the front. |

5A Finding Meanings

Choose two phrases to form a sentence that correctly uses a word from Word List 5. Write each sentence in the space provided.

audacious
confiscate
conscientious
depict
embark
inkling
lackadaisical
mutiny
pilfer
profusion
prudent
rankle
rebuke
serene
slovenly

1. (a) one that is peaceful.
   (b) one that changes frequently.
   (c) A lackadaisical manner is
   (d) A serene manner is

2. (a) To rankle someone is to
   (b) To rebuke someone is to
   (c) warn that person.
   (d) criticize that person.

3. (a) a feeling of mistrust.
   (b) Prudence is
   (c) Audacity is
   (d) excessive boldness.

4. (a) to describe it.
   (b) to remember it.
   (c) To confiscate something is
   (d) To depict something is

5. (a) imitate another's actions.
   (b) set out on a voyage.
   (c) To embark is to
   (d) To mutiny is to

6. (a) avoids unnecessary risks.   (c) A slovenly plan is one that
   (b) A prudent plan is one that   (d) has several parts.

7. (a) To pilfer something is to   (c) take it by force.
   (b) To confiscate something is to   (d) exchange it for something else.

8. (a) A conscientious person is one who (c) defies authority.
   (b) A lackadaisical person is one who (d) does careful work.

9. (a) to rebel against authority.   (c) to make a sincere effort.
   (b) To mutiny is   (d) To pilfer is

10. (a) they are numerous.   (c) If the illustrations are profuse
    (b) If the illustrations are slovenly (d) they are elegant.

5B Just the Right Word

Improve each of the following sentences by crossing out the bold phrase and replacing it with a word (or a form of the word) from Word List 5.

1. Spencer was **so willing to take risks** with his bicycle that his parents feared he would hurt himself.

2. My sister is always accusing me of being very **untidy and careless** in my personal habits.

3. Poison ivy grows in **very large amounts** at the southern end of the island.

4. When making loans, bankers are expected to act with **care to avoid anything that might be too risky**.

5. **An act of defiance against one's superior** is a serious crime.

6. Unlike many of the early colonists, Roger Williams, acting in a **principled and honest** manner, paid the Narragansetts for the land he wanted to occupy.

7. Helena had the first **faint suggestions** she had won the election when reporters arrived.

8. I hope you are not a person for whom an imagined slight **continues to irritate** just as much as a real one.

9. The dance committee was so **lacking in enthusiasm** that a week before the event nothing had been arranged.

10. Before mountaineers can **take the first steps** on a major climbing expedition, they need to raise money for equipment and supplies.

5C Applying Meanings

Circle the letter of each correct answer to the questions below. Questions may have more than one correct answer.

1. Which of the following indicates a **slovenly** person?
   (a) polished shoes   (c) dirty fingernails
   (b) long hair   (d) patched jeans

2. Which of the following might deserve a **rebuke?**
   (a) breaking a rule   (c) saving a child's life
   (b) showing negligence   (d) getting an A on a test

3. Which of the following might **rankle?**
   (a) a deliberate insult   (c) an unexpected rebuff
   (b) a false accusation   (d) an affable remark

4. Which of the following could be **confiscated?**
   (a) a warm smile   (c) a helpful attitude
   (b) a sum of money   (d) a firm promise

5. Which of the following might a **lackadaisical** student do?
   (a) ask for extra homework (c) pay close attention
   (b) get straight A's   (d) daydream in class

6. Which of the following would a **conscientious** driver do?
   (a) signal before making a turn   (c) obey speed limits
   (b) stay alert while at the wheel (d) ignore stop signs

7. Which of the following suggests **serenity?**
   (a) a basketball game   (c) a sleeping baby
   (b) a sunset   (d) a carnival ride

8. Which of the following can a person **pilfer?**
   (a) a diamond ring   (c) a candy bar
   (b) a car   (d) a sneeze

audacious

confiscate

conscientious

depict

embark

inkling

lackadaisical

mutiny

pilfer

profusion

prudent

rankle

rebuke

serene

slovenly

5D Word Study

Write in the missing word in the sentences below. Choose each word from this or an earlier lesson.

1. The prefix *re-* means "back." It combines with the Latin verb *salire* (to leap) to form the English word _____ (able to spring back).

2. The prefix *re-* also means "again." It combines with the Latin verb *currere* (to run) to form the English word _____ (to happen again).

3. The prefix *de-* means "remove." It combines with the Greek word *hydr* (water) to form the English word _____ (to remove water from).

4. The prefix *an-* means "without." It combines with the Greek word *onuma* (name) to form the English word ____anonumous____ (of an unknown name).

5. The Greek word *pseudes* means "false." Combined with the Greek word for "name," it forms the English word _____ (a fictitious or pen name).

6. Two Greek words, *anthos,* meaning "flower," and *legein,* meaning "to gather," combine to form the English word _____ (a collection of various writings).

7. The prefix *in-* means "in" or "into." It changes to *im-* when it combines with the Latin verb *pellare* (to drive) to form the English word _____ (to drive forward).

5E Passage

Read the passage below; then complete the exercise that follows.

The *Bounty,* Part One

When the captain of His Majesty's Ship *Bounty* spoke to the men on watch a little after midnight, everything seemed normal. Three weeks before, on April 4, 1789, Captain Bligh and his crew had **embarked** for the West Indies from the tropical South Pacific island of Tahiti. For six months, they had collected breadfruit plants, which grew in **profusion** on Tahiti. The purpose of the voyage was to transport over a thousand of these plants, already carefully stowed on board, to the West Indies to be grown as a food crop for the slaves who worked on the large plantations there.

Captain Bligh probably should have realized that not all was as **serene** as it seemed. He knew that his men had been loath to leave the pleasant island life to return to the more rigid structure of life aboard ship. He had, in fact, been dissatisfied with the **slovenly** habits they had developed while the *Bounty* had lain at anchor. Not only had some of the crew failed to care properly for the sails, but others had **pilfered** from the ship because no one was keeping proper watches.

Furthermore, Captain Bligh seemed to have lost confidence in his chief mate, Fletcher Christian. It had been Christian's **lackadaisical** attitude, Bligh believed, that had resulted in the sailors' neglecting their duties on Tahiti. Bligh had **rebuked** Christian for failing to supervise the men properly. If this had **rankled** the chief mate, Bligh had not perceived any change in him when the two had dined together.

Despite these annoyances, Bligh's mood was calm when he returned to his cabin. He had no **inkling** of what was about to happen as, rocked by the gentle motion of the ship, he fell asleep. Had he been **prudent**, he might have posted a guard outside his cabin. As it was, its door was not even locked. Shortly before dawn, the captain was awakened abruptly. Fletcher Christian, accompanied by several crew members, burst in and informed him that they had taken over the ship. They had **confiscated** all the weapons on board and locked up the eighteen crew members who remained loyal to the captain.

Bligh warned those who held him prisoner that for this **audacious** act they would all be hanged. His warning, however, had no effect. Later that morning, he and the loyal crew members were pushed into an open boat. They were permitted to take some weapons with them and were given a small quantity of food and water. Bligh watched helplessly as Christian and the remaining crew members on board sailed off in the *Bounty,* leaving him and the other passengers in the tiny boat to their fate in the middle of the vast ocean.

• • • •

Three movies have been made of the **mutiny** that took place on the *Bounty* on the morning of April 28, 1789. All three **depict** Captain Bligh as a cruel man who treated his crew badly and was himself responsible for what happened. However, by using information in court documents, letters, and diaries written by people who participated in the events, several historians argue that Bligh was a **conscientious** naval officer, no stricter than other sea captains of the time. While he had ordered several men flogged twelve or even twenty-four lashes for being disobedient, this was the usual punishment at that time in the British navy for quite minor offenses. To this day, there is no unanimous explanation for this event that changed the lives of these men forever.

Answer each of the following questions in the form of a sentence. If a question does not contain a vocabulary word from this lesson's word list, use one in your answer. Use each word only once. Questions and answers will then contain all fifteen words (or forms of the words).

audacious
confiscate
conscientious
depict
embark
inkling
lackadaisical
mutiny
pilfer
profusion
prudent
rankle
rebuke
serene
slovenly

1. Why do you think there was such a serious punishment for **mutiny**?

_____

2. Why would it be inaccurate to describe Fletcher Christian as a **conscientious** first mate?

_____

3. What is one example from the passage that illustrates the crew's **slovenly** performance?

_____

4. Why do you suppose Christian was **rebuked** but not flogged for his supervision of the men on Tahiti?

_____

5. What is the meaning of **embarked** as it is used in the passage?

_____

6. What kinds of things do you think the men could have **pilfered** from the ship?

7. Why was Tahiti a good place to gather breadfruit plants?

8. What details in the passage show that Bligh was not **lackadaisical** about running his ship?

9. Why would it be inaccurate to say that the men who took over the ship were acting in a **prudent** manner?

10. Was Bligh **rankled** by his men's behavior on the night of April 27, 1789? Explain.

11. Why is it likely that Captain Bligh did not feel **serene** as he watched the *Bounty* sail away?

12. How did Fletcher Christian make sure that none of the crew would resist his takeover?

13. How do we know that no one warned the captain of possible trouble?

14. What is the meaning of **audacious** as it is used in the passage?

15. Why do you think Captain Bligh was **depicted** as cruel in the movies about this event?

FUN & FASCINATING FACTS

In early Roman times, tax collectors working for the state put the money they collected in baskets woven from rushes. The Latin name for this basket was *fiscus*. *Fiscal*, which means "having to do with money collected and spent by the state," is formed from *fiscus*. So is the word **confiscate**. The state has the power to seize, by force if necessary, money owed to it by its citizens.

The word **lackadaisical** has an interesting history. In the eighteenth century, a person might express regret for a failure to act properly by saying, "Alack the day." Translated into modern English it means, "I'm sorry that day happened." The expression became shortened to "lackaday," and a person who had reason to use it frequently was described as *lackadaisical*.

Lax is a separate word, meaning "not strict or demanding." (Accidents occurred because of the *lax* safety rules at the plant.) Don't substitute *laxadaisical*, which is not in any dictionary, for *lackadaisical*.

Lesson 6

Word List
Study the definitions of the words below; then do the exercises for the lesson.

anarchy
an´ ər kē

n. 1. Total absence of government.
Government officials fled, leaving the country in a state of **anarchy**.
2. Lack of order; total confusion.
After the 2003 Iraq war, the country was in a state of **anarchy** with no established law enforcement in place.

apprehend
ap rē hend´

v. 1. To seize; to arrest.
John Brown was **apprehended** when he tried to confiscate guns at Harper's Ferry, Virginia in 1859.
2. To grasp the meaning of; to understand.
When contact with the space shuttle *Columbia* was lost on February 1, 2003, those tracking it **apprehended** at once what had happened.

arraign
ə rān´

v. To bring before a court to face charges.
Lee Harvey Oswald had barely been **arraigned** for the assassination of the president when he too was shot and killed.

assimilate
ə sim´ ə lāt

v. 1. To absorb into a population.
By the second generation, the Cambodian immigrants had been **assimilated** into Canadian society.
2. To take in a part and absorb into the whole.
The students **assimilated** the new information, then began to apply it.

bizarre
bi zär´

adj. Strikingly out of the ordinary; peculiar.
The smashed and twisted automobile, resting in a bed of violets near the side of the road, created a **bizarre** image.

calamity
kə lam´ ə tē

n. An event that causes great suffering and harm; a disaster.
The train engineer averted a **calamity** by slamming on the brakes as soon as he saw the car stalled on the tracks.
calamitous *adj.* Disastrous.
Filling in these wetlands to build a mall has been **calamitous** for the songbirds that migrated here each year.

conspire
kən spīr´

v. 1. To plan together secretly to do something wrong or illegal.
Campaign workers **conspired** to break into their opponent's headquarters.
2. To join or act together.
The beautiful weather, good friends, and delicious food **conspired** to make the weekend at the beach one I will always remember.
conspiracy *n.* (kən spir´ ə sē) A joining with others to plan or carry out unlawful acts.
The **conspiracy** of the German officers to kill Hitler failed on July 20, 1944.

dissension
di sen´ shən

n. A difference of opinion; disagreement.
As representatives worked on the Constitution that hot summer of 1787, **dissension** over power for the states versus power for the federal government grew.

elapse
ē laps´

v. To pass or slip by (used with time).
Five years **elapsed** before they saw their cousins again.

imminent
im´ ə nənt

adj. About to happen; likely to occur in the very near future.
The clouds rolling in made rain seem **imminent**.

interrogate
in ter´ ə gāt

v. To ask questions of, especially in a thorough or formal manner.
The police will **interrogate** the suspects separately in order to compare their stories.
interrogation *n.* The act of questioning.
Helen's lawyer was present during the **interrogation** of the witness to the accident.

lionize
lī´ ə nīz

v. To treat as a celebrity.
After he made the first solo transatlantic flight, Charles Lindbergh was **lionized**.

meticulous
mə tik´ yə ləs

adj. Extremely careful; attentive to small details.
All of the parachutists gave their gear a **meticulous** final check before leaping from the plane.

shackle
shak´ əl

n. 1. A ring or band put around the arm or leg to prevent free movement.
In the 1800s, Africans captured for the slave trade were crammed into ships where they sat in **shackles** for the duration of the voyage to America.
2. Something that prevents free action.
Kevin hoped he could throw off the **shackles** of parental control when he left for college.
v. To prevent freedom of action.
High school dropouts often find that their lack of education **shackles** them to low-paying jobs.

swelter
swel´ tər

v. To suffer from or to be overcome by great heat.
We **sweltered** in the hot sun because there was no shade in the fields where we worked.
sweltering *adj.* Very hot and humid; uncomfortable because of extremely hot weather.
Going for a swim is the best way to cool down on a **sweltering** July day.

anarchy

apprehend

arraign

assimilate

bizarre

calamity

conspire

dissension

elapse

imminent

interrogate

lionize

meticulous

shackle

swelter

6A Finding Meanings

Choose two phrases to form a sentence that correctly uses a word from Word List 6. Write each sentence in the space provided.

1. (a) restricts free movement.
   (b) causes great joy.
   (c) A calamity is something that
   (d) A shackle is something that

2. (a) question that person closely.
   (b) To interrogate someone is to
   (c) To apprehend someone is to
   (d) fear that person.

3. (a) be uncomfortably hot.
   (b) break up into smaller parts.
   (c) To swelter is to
   (d) To elapse is to

4. (a) Dissension is   (c) a total absence of government.
   (b) fear of what might happen.   (d) Anarchy is

5. (a) A calamity is   (c) a lifting of all restraint.
   (b) A conspiracy is   (d) an event that causes great suffering.

6. (a) To recur   (c) is to agree.
   (b) is to understand.   (d) To apprehend

7. (a) To lionize someone is to   (c) treat that person as a hero or heroine.
   (b) To arraign someone is to   (d) to make that person angry.

8. (a) is one that keeps recurring.   (c) is one that is very peculiar.
   (b) An imminent event   (d) A bizarre event

9. (a) To arraign some people is to   (c) To assimilate some people is to
   (b) absorb them into a larger group.   (d) show that they are innocent.

10. (a) To elapse is to   (c) fail to do what is expected or required.
    (b) To conspire is to   (d) plan secretly or illegally with others.

6B Just the Right Word

Improve each of the following sentences by crossing out the bold phrase and replacing it with a word (or a form of the word) from Word List 6.

1. The roots of trees **take in and absorb** water from the soil.

2. Janine, seeing that an accident was **about to happen in the very near future**, moved her baby brother away from the stove.

3. As we examined the ancient Peruvian embroideries, we were amazed by how **extremely careful and attentive to small details** the creators of these pieces had been.

4. Our teachers always encouraged us to finish high school because no one, they said, should be **prevented from doing what they wished** by the lack of education.

5. To avoid **a complete breakdown in government,** the president called for a new election and then resigned.

6. **Strong disagreement** about whether or not to permit the use of trail bikes in the state park flared up at the town meeting.

7. Margaret finished the test well before the thirty minutes had **slipped by**.

8. John D. Rockefeller, Jr., with the managers of the Colorado mine, **secretly made plans** to prevent the union leaders from entering the work area.

9. Rebecca remembered summers on a Maine lake, away from the **very hot and uncomfortable** city.

10. The Bill of Rights gives both citizens and noncitizens the right to have a lawyer represent them when being **called before a court to answer charges**.

6C Applying Meanings

Circle the letter of each correct answer to the questions below. Questions may have more than one correct answer.

anarchy
apprehend
arraign
assimilate
bizarre
calamity
conspire
dissension
elapse
imminent
interrogate
lionize
meticulous
shackle
swelter

1. Which of the following could **shackle** a person?
   - (a) fear
   - (b) leg irons
   - (c) education
   - (d) responsibility

2. Which of the following might be considered **bizarre**?
   - (a) a dancing llama
   - (b) a July snowstorm
   - (c) an all-black zebra
   - (d) twins with different birthdays

3. Which of the following might be **apprehended**?
   - (a) a poem's meaning
   - (b) a profound utterance
   - (c) a runaway child
   - (d) a coded message

4. In which of the following might **dissension** occur?
   - (a) a club
   - (b) a nation
   - (c) an army
   - (d) an individual

5. Which of the following could be **imminent**?
   - (a) yesterday
   - (b) a blizzard
   - (c) a hurricane
   - (d) the 1920s

6. Which of the following might be **lionized**?

    (a) an Olympic gold medalist   (c) an anonymous poet

    (b) a movie star   (d) a great white shark

7. Which of the following describes a **conspiracy**?

    (a) It is secret.   (c) It involves just one person.

    (b) It is possibly illegal.   (d) It occurs spontaneously.

8. Which of the following could be **calamitous**?

    (a) an earthquake   (c) a flood

    (b) a toothache   (d) a shipwreck

6D Word Study

In each of the groups below, circle the two words that are synonyms.

1. meticulous	afraid	bizarre	careful
2. assimilate	bind	interrogate	absorb
3. anarchy	guile	calamity	disaster
4. shackle	pass	elapse	suggest
5. apprehend	arraign	charge	confiscate
6. sweltering	peculiar	imminent	bizarre

In each of the groups below, circle the two words that are antonyms.

7. conspiracy	order	entreaty	anarchy
8. succumb	shackle	resist	interrogate
9. chilly	serene	odd	sweltering
10. dissension	confusion	agreement	conjecture

6E Passage

Read the passage below; then complete the exercise that follows.

The *Bounty*, Part Two

After Captain Bligh and the eighteen members of his crew who remained loyal to him were set adrift in an open boat, they understood clearly that the chance of their surviving to report the **calamity** was slim. Nevertheless, Bligh wasted no time in raising the sail and ordering the men to start rowing. He also began a journal, in which he **meticulously** recorded everything that happened.

The greatest hazard they faced was the weather. In stormy seas the overcrowded twenty-three-foot boat was tossed so mercilessly that drowning seemed **imminent**. One storm, which lasted two weeks, kept the men thoroughly soaked the entire time. On other days, the **sweltering** heat of the tropical sun left them too exhausted to row. They stayed alive by collecting rainwater and by stopping at tiny, uninhabited islands to gather fruit and oysters. In this way they added to the meager supply of food and water they had been given when they were set adrift.

At last, weak and barely alive, they reached Timor, north of Australia, where they were received by the Dutch governor of the island. Their ordeal had lasted forty-one days. Another ten weeks **elapsed** before Captain Bligh was well enough to leave for England. When he arrived there in March 1790, he was **lionized** by the public for his amazing feat of crossing almost four thousand miles of uncharted ocean in an open boat. Nevertheless, losing one's ship as the result of a mutiny was a serious matter that required investigation. Bligh defended his actions well before the court of inquiry, which was conducted by the navy. They ruled that he was not responsible for the loss of his ship.

The British government took a quite different view of the mutineers, however. Having learned that some of the former crew members of the *Bounty* were on Tahiti, the navy sent an armed ship, the *Pandora,* to bring them to justice. When the ship arrived in March 1791, the officers found that many of the mutineers had married Tahitian women and were beginning to **assimilate** into the life of the island. All the men were quickly **apprehended** and taken aboard the *Pandora,* where they were **interrogated** by the captain. They told him that Fletcher Christian, with eight crew members, had sailed away to an unknown destination after a brief stay on Tahiti.

With the captured mutineers on board, the *Pandora* set sail for England. On the return voyage, however, four of the prisoners drowned when the ship sank in a storm. They had been kept **shackled** below decks, with the captain refusing to release them until the last moment before the ship went down. Of those remaining, six were **arraigned** when they eventually reached England. At the trial that followed, three were found guilty and hanged for **conspiring** to take over the *Bounty* by force. The others were set free.

And yet the story does not end there. In 1808, an American seal-hunting ship called the *Topaz* dropped anchor off what was believed to be an uninhabited island thirteen hundred miles southeast of Tahiti. A party sent ashore to explore discovered a man there named Alexander Smith. He had been one of the mutineers on the *Bounty,* and he had a **bizarre** tale to tell the American sailors.

Twenty years before, he said, Fletcher Christian had sailed to this speck of land, known today as Pitcairn Island, accompanied by eight of his fellow mutineers and eighteen Tahitians. After the *Bounty* had burned and sunk, the men and women began their new life on the island. But **dissension** soon developed when the sailors tried to force the Tahitians to become their servants. Quarrels led to violence and eventually to murder. The society they had established collapsed into **anarchy**. Within ten years of the *Bounty's* arrival at the island, Alexander Smith was the only one of the men left alive. Today, his descendants still live on Pitcairn Island.

anarchy

apprehend

arraign

assimilate

bizarre

calamity

conspire

dissension

elapse

imminent

interrogate

lionize

meticulous

shackle

swelter

Answer each of the following questions in the form of a sentence. If a question does not contain a vocabulary word from this lesson's word list, use one in your answer. Use each word only once. Questions and answers will then contain all fifteen words (or forms of the words).

1. Why wasn't Captain Bligh ever **arraigned**?

2. In what ways did the tropical weather create problems for the men in the open boat?

3. Why would the navy have wanted to **interrogate** Bligh once he had returned to England?

4. What do we know what happened to Bligh and his crew after they were set adrift?

5. How does the passage make clear that Bligh and his men did not believe their rescue was **imminent**?

6. Why do you think there was no **anarchy** on the overcrowded open boat?

7. Why might the sailors from the *Topaz* have doubted Alexander Smith's story?

8. Why do you think Christian left Tahiti in the *Bounty*?

9. Why was Captain Bligh **lionized** by the English public?

10. Describe the relations among the residents of Pitcairn Island.

11. What **calamity** befell the *Pandora*?

12. How do you know the mutineers were trying to become **assimilated** into Tahitian society?

13. What restrictions did the prisoners on the *Pandora* experience?

14. Following his return to Tahiti, how much time passed before Christian again sailed away?

15. What was the nature of the **conspiracy** for which three of the sailors were hanged?

FUN & FASCINATING FACTS

The Latin verb *prehendere* means "to grasp" or "to seize" and forms the root of the verb **apprehend**. Other words formed from this root include: *comprehend*, "to understand; to grasp what is being explained." (You seem unable to *comprehend* the seriousness of what you have done.); *prehensile*, "able to grip." (A monkey's *prehensile* tail acts as a fifth limb.); *apprehensive*, "concerned" or "afraid." (An *apprehensive* person is gripped by a feeling of nervousness.)

Lesson 7

Word List

Study the definitions of the words below; then do the exercises for the lesson.

claustrophobia
klôs trə fō´ bē ə

n. An abnormal fear of narrow, enclosed spaces.
Although John is in the navy, his **claustrophobia** prevents him from serving in submarines.

colleague
käl´ ēg

n. An associate or coworker of similar status.
On her birthday, Mom's **colleagues** surprised her by taking her out to lunch.

condescend
kän də send´

v. 1. To lower oneself to a position one considers inferior.
Once he became president of the company, Mr. Rose never **condescended** to travel in any way but first class.
2. To behave in an offensively superior manner.
During rehearsals, the star of the show never **condescended** to join the rest of the cast for lunch; instead he ate alone in his dressing room.
condescending *adj.* Showing an offensively superior manner.
Lucinda's **condescending** attitude is not what we want in our elementary school tutors.

contingent
kən tin´ jənt

adj. 1. Conditional; depending on something else.
Tanya's plans for attending the university were **contingent** on receiving a scholarship.
2. Likely, but not certain to happen; possible.
If it rains, our **contingent** plan is to move the strawberry festival from the school lawn to the auditorium.
n. A group that is part of a larger one.
The Ethiopian **contingent** led the parade of Olympic athletes into the stadium.

daunt
dônt

v. To discourage or intimidate.
Learning that she needed a bone-marrow transplant did not **daunt** Miranda, but instead gave her hope for her future.
daunting *adj.* So difficult or dangerous as to discourage or intimidate.
Expelled from Massachusetts Bay Colony in the winter of 1636, Roger Williams began a **daunting** journey south to find a place to settle.

deluge
del´ yōōj

n. 1. A downpour of rain; a flood.
Opening the dam just north of the Grand Canyon sent a **deluge** to the dry river beds in the canyon.
2. A flood of anything.
When the Millers advertised their new car for such a low price, they received a **deluge** of offers to buy.
v. To flood or overwhelm.
As she convalesced from her surgery, Delia's friends **deluged** her with cards, phone calls, and visits.

dispel
di spel´

v. To clear away; to remove or get rid of, as if by scattering.
I wanted Linda to reassure me, but her letter, instead of **dispelling** my fears, increased them.

dub
dub

v. To give a title, nickname, or description to.
His fans **dubbed** Babe Ruth "the Sultan of Swat."

fanfare
fan´ fâr

n. 1. A sounding of trumpets or other brass instruments.
The audience is alerted to the entrance on-stage of Hamlet's mother, Queen Gertrude, by a loud **fanfare**.
2. Any showy display.
The props manager, working behind the scenes without **fanfare**, was essential to the overall effect of the play.

fledgling
flej´ liŋ

n. 1. A young bird just learning to fly.
The **fledgling** swallows took short trial flights over the yard from their nest on the porch.
2. A young and inexperienced person.
The reporter, a **fledgling**, forgot to get the eyewitness's name.
adj. New and untested.
My father's **fledgling** computer programming business has been very busy this month.

inane
in ān´

adj. Empty; shallow or silly.
Susan, bored by the **inane** chatter of her classmates, walked on down the hall.
inanity *n.* (in an´ ə tē) Foolishness; a silly or pointless act.
Hearing the **inanity** of his own response made Bruno understand how exhausted and in need of sleep he really was.

mettle
met´ l

n. Courage to bear up under difficult circumstances; spirit.
In spite of the soldiers' threats, the children showed their **mettle** by refusing to tell them anything about their friend.

negligible
neg´ lə jə bəl

adj. Small and unimportant, not worth noticing.
The team's mistakes in the final tournament were **negligible**, having no effect on the result.

protract
prō trakt´

v. To draw out or lengthen (in time).
Our trip was **protracted** unnecessarily by driving right past the correct exit.

replica
rep´ li kə

n. A copy or reproduction, especially one on a smaller scale than the original.
A **replica** of the Statue of Liberty stood on my grandmother's shelf, a reminder of her first glimpse of her new country.

claustrophobia
colleague
condescend
contingent
daunt
deluge
dispel
dub
fanfare
fledgling
inane
mettle
negligible
protract
replica

7A Finding Meanings

Choose two phrases to form a sentence that correctly uses a word from Word List 7. Write each sentence in the space provided.

1. (a) A contingent is
   (b) A colleague is
   (c) a coworker with equal status.
   (d) an inexperienced person.

2. (a) fear of enclosed spaces.
   (b) Mettle is
   (c) a breakdown of the social order.
   (d) Claustrophobia is

3. (a) a large amount of it.
   (b) A replica of something is
   (c) A deluge of something is
   (d) a showy display of it.

4. (a) a part of a larger group.
   (b) A fanfare is

   (c) a fixed period of time.
   (d) A contingent is

5. (a) A condescending actor
   (b) A fledgling actor

   (c) is one who outshines all others.
   (d) is one who treats others as inferior.

6. (a) a lack of spirit.
   (b) An inanity is

   (c) A fanfare is
   (d) a flourish of trumpets.

7. (a) fail to take proper care.
   (b) To be daunted is to

   (c) be afraid or intimidated.
   (d) To be negligible is to

8. (a) a young bird.
   (b) A fledgling is

   (c) A replica is
   (d) a feather worn as decoration.

9. (a) one that offers encouragement.
   (b) one that is foolish.

   (c) A negligible remark is
   (d) An inane remark is

10. (a) If an argument is protracted,
    (b) it is kept from damage or harm.

    (c) If an argument is dispelled,
    (d) it is drawn out in time.

7B Just the Right Word

Improve each of the following sentences by crossing out the bold phrase and replacing it with a word (or a form of the word) from Word List 7.

1. Your salary will be **dependent to some extent** on how many years of experience as a nurse you have had.

2. A **somewhat smaller copy** of Philadelphia's Liberty Bell hangs in our town museum.

3. **Young and inexperienced** fencers need close supervision at first, so that they do not hurt each other with their foils.

4. The cost of an oil change for the car was **small enough that we thought nothing of it**.

5. With very little **display intended to gain attention**, the owner announced that he would continue to pay his workers while the burned factory building was repaired.

6. When Brad and Tom got caught in a blizzard with the herd of horses they were driving over the mountain, they had plenty of opportunities to show their **ability to bear up under difficult circumstances.**

7. The sudden **downpour of rain** caused the crowd at the racetrack to run for shelter.

8. On summer mornings, the ocean breeze soon **gets rid of** the morning mist.

9. Last summer the lifeguard at our pool was **given the name** Hercules because he loved to show off his muscles.

10. The way to deal with the **silly foolishness** of daytime talk shows is to turn off the television.

7C Applying Meanings

Circle the letter of each correct answer to the questions below. Questions may have more than one correct answer.

1. Of which of the following could a **replica** be made?
   - (a) a rebuff
   - (b) the *Bounty*
   - (c) an ancient coin
   - (d) a dinosaur bone

claustrophobia

colleague

condescend

2. Which of the following could be called a **fledgling?**
   - (a) a day-old chick
   - (b) an inexperienced waiter
   - (c) a robin testing its wings
   - (d) a two-star general

contingent

daunt

deluge

3. Which of the following can be **condescending?**
   - (a) a remark
   - (b) an attitude
   - (c) a person
   - (d) an elevator

dispel

dub

fanfare

4. With which of the following can one be **deluged?**
   - (a) offers
   - (b) mail
   - (c) orders
   - (d) water

fledgling

inane

mettle

5. Which of the following would have **colleagues?**
   - (a) a doctor
   - (b) a lawyer
   - (c) a recluse
   - (d) a college professor

negligible

protract

replica

6. Which of the following might a person suffering from **claustrophobia** avoid?

    (a) open spaces   (c) elevators

    (b) heights   (d) narrow tunnels

7. Which of the following could be **negligible**?

    (a) an amount of time lost   (c) a sum of money

    (b) a careless driver   (d) an amount of damage

8. Which of the following can be **dispelled**?

    (a) fear   (c) doubts

    (b) suspicion   (d) fog

7D Word Study

Each group of four words below contains two words that are either synonyms or antonyms. Circle these two words; then circle the *S* if they are synonyms, the *A* if they are antonyms.

1. annoy	name	deluge	dub	S	A
2. fanfare	courage	welcome	mettle	S	A
3. rankle	shorten	protract	deluge	S	A
4. condescend	frighten	daunt	lengthen	S	A
5. contingent	expert	colleague	fledgling	S	A
6. conspire	dispel	condescend	evoke	S	A
7. foolish	inane	negligible	cursory	S	A
8. deluge	copy	address	replica	S	A
9. negligible	meticulous	substantial	gruesome	S	A
10. proprietor	associate	colleague	expert	S	A

Read the passage below; then complete the exercise that follows.

Women in Space, Part One

In 1959, the National Aeronautics and Space Administration (NASA) introduced the first seven United States astronauts to the public. The announcement, made with great **fanfare**, brought instant fame to the seven. All were former test pilots and all were male.

In 1978, almost twenty years later, when the newest **contingent** of aspiring astronauts arrived for training at the Johnson Space Center in Houston, things had changed. That group included scientists, engineers, and medical doctors. In addition, six of the thirty-five **fledgling** astronauts were women.

At first, a **condescending** attitude toward women in the space program by some of the older men presented a problem. These space veterans felt that women lacked "the right stuff" to be astronauts. To **dispel** such prejudices, the women felt that they needed to perform as well or better than their male counterparts. Candidates had to be smart, tough, highly educated, and meticulous in everything they did. Physical strength, the one area where the men could outperform the women, was not an important factor. During their year of basic training, the six women met the challenge, proving their **mettle** in all situations.

Training to be an astronaut was a **daunting** task. The astronauts studied a range of subjects, including astronomy, the weather, geology, mathematics, navigation, and the human body. They spent hundreds of hours in the classroom learning the inner workings of every part of the space shuttle. Then they received hands-on experience in a **replica** of the shuttle, complete in even the smallest detail. In this way the actual space shuttle was comfortingly familiar to the astronauts, even when going aboard for the first time.

Trainee astronauts spent time underwater to simulate the effects of weightlessness that they would experience in space. They also went aboard K-135 planes that flew almost vertically upward before turning back along a **protracted** flight path that curved toward the earth, resulting in a sensation of weightlessness. These flights also gave other sensations, which led to the trainees **dubbing** this aircraft "the vomit comet."

Another important part of the program was survival training, both on land and at sea. What if the space shuttle's rocket engines and their backup systems failed while it was in orbit? Even though the chance of this happening was **negligible**, the astronauts had to be prepared for every possibility. Aboard the shuttle were fabric rescue balls, thirty inches in diameter, which could be inflated with oxygen. In an emergency, astronauts would crawl inside them while waiting to be transferred to a rescue vehicle. Climbing into one of these was very unpleasant, especially for anyone suffering even a mild form of **claustrophobia**.

Finally, in the spring of 1982, one of the six women graduates of the space program was chosen for Space Transportation System-Flight 7. She was Sally Ride, a scientist with an advanced degree in physics from Stanford University and an expert in X-ray astronomy and lasers. As soon as the announcement was made, NASA was **deluged** with requests for interviews with the first American woman to fly in space. Dr. Ride cheerfully submitted to endless questioning from reporters, answering even the most **inane** ones with patience and good humor.

After the flood of publicity came a further year of intensive training geared to the requirements of the mission for which she had been chosen. Then, on June 18, 1983, along with four male **colleagues**, Dr. Sally Ride began her historic five-day flight aboard the space shuttle *Challenger*.

claustrophobia
colleague
condescend
contingent
daunt
deluge
dispel
dub
fanfare
fledgling
inane
mettle
negligible
protract
replica

Answer each of the following questions in the form of a sentence. If a question does not contain a vocabulary word from this lesson's word list, use one in your answer. Use each word only once. Questions and answers will then contain all fifteen words (or forms of the words).

1. How did the women trainees **dispel** any doubts about their abilities?

2. Why would the space shuttle seem familiar to those boarding it for the first time?

3. What is the meaning of **contingent** as it is used in the passage?

4. Which part of the training would you find **daunting**?

5. How important is physical strength for astronauts?

6. Were women able to succeed in all areas of the training? Explain your answer.

7. Why would someone who was afraid of enclosed spaces be unhappy as an astronaut?

8. What is the meaning of **fanfare** as it is used in the passage?

9. How many women trained along with Dr. Ride?

10. What caused Dr. Ride's training to be **protracted**?

11. Why do you think reporters ask celebrities **inane** questions?

12. Why would it be inaccurate to say that the older male astronauts welcomed the female trainees?

13. What pet name did the trainees have for the K-135 plane?

14. What is the meaning of **deluge** as it is used in the passage?

15. Would it be accurate to describe Sally Ride as a **fledgling** astronaut when she was chosen for Flight-7? Explain your answer.

FUN & FASCINATING FACTS

Old Norse was a northern European language spoken in Scandinavia until the fourteenth century. The Old Norse word *dubben* means "to strike" and was given a particular meaning when it was brought into English. A monarch, in the act of naming a person a knight, would strike that person lightly on the shoulder with a sword, while saying, "I **dub** thee Sir _____," along with the person's name. The word came to mean "to give a title to" and was later broadened to its present, more general, meaning.

Lesson 8

Word List
Study the definitions of the words below; then do the exercises for the lesson.

adept
ə dept´

adj. Highly skilled; expert.
Odgen Nash's poems reveal how **adept** he was at writing comic verse.

audible
ô´ də bəl

adj. Capable of being heard.
The sound of the harp was barely **audible** in the large hall.

azure
azh´ ər

n. and *adj.* The blue color of a cloudless sky.
The **azure** of Caribbean waters is in striking contrast to the grayish green of more northern seas.

banter
ban´ tər

v. To exchange playful, teasing remarks.
The opposing players **bantered** nervously before the soccer match.
n. Light, playful conversation.
The backstage **banter** among the actors ended abruptly when the curtain rose for the first act.

capacious
kə pā´ shəs

adj. Able to hold a large amount; roomy.
The **capacious** closets of their new apartment would provide enough room for the clothes of her two teenagers, Mrs. Winters decided.

copious
kō´ pē əs

adj. Large in quantity; abundant.
Mediterranean cooking uses **copious** amounts of olive oil.

crucial
krōō´ shəl

adj. Extremely important; vital in resolving something.
This canceled check, which shows the date Raquel sent the money, was **crucial** to establishing that she paid her rent on time.

decelerate
dē sel´ ə rāt

v. To slow down or to cause to slow down.
Reverse thrust applied to the engines after landing causes the aircraft to **decelerate**.

deploy
di ploi´

v. 1. To arrange troops or equipment in position for battle.
Artillery had been **deployed** around Sarajevo for two years before it was withdrawn as part of the cease-fire.
2. To put into use.
When the new art center was completely finished, the editor **deployed** three reporters to cover the dedication.

facilitate
fə sil´ ə tāt

v. To make easier.
Living in Peru for two years **facilitated** my learning Spanish.

fastidious
fa stid´ ē əs

adj. 1. Paying close attention to detail.
The mustard stain on his sweater suggested to Lilly that Simon was not as **fastidious** about his clothes as about his car, which was spotless.
2. Difficult to please.
My **fastidious** friend Dignora will allow her friends to enter her room only after they have removed their shoes.

fitful fit´ fəl	*adj.* Not steady; irregular. After a **fitful** sleep in my hotel room, which faced the highway, I awoke feeling groggy and unprepared for the first day of the conference.
grapple grap´ əl	*v.* 1. To struggle with in close combat; to wrestle. Jake **grappled** with the intruders, but they fled before help arrived. 2. To come to grips with. The community **grappled** with the problem of improving the quality of education in their schools. *n.* An iron shaft with a claw for grasping and holding things. The captain threw the **grapple**, hooking the abandoned vessel, and then drew it close enough to board.
pang paŋ	*n.* A sudden sharp feeling of pain or distress. Jarvis felt a **pang** of regret when he sold his old car.
precede prē sēd´	*v.* To go or come before in time, rank, or position. In France, the simpler Romanesque style of architecture **preceded** the more elaborate Gothic style.

8A Finding Meanings

Choose two phrases to form a sentence that correctly uses a word from Word List 8. Write each sentence in the space provided.

1. (a) A fastidious employee
   (b) is one who is fussy about details.
   (c) is one who can be easily replaced.
   (d) A crucial employee

_____

2. (a) large in amount.
   (b) Audible rainfall is
   (c) Copious rainfall is
   (d) starting and stopping regularly.

_____

3. (a) To decelerate auto production
   (b) To facilitate auto production
   (c) is to make it easier.
   (d) is to conclude it.

_____

4. (a) broken and irregular.
   (b) Audible breathing is
   (c) rapid but shallow.
   (d) Fitful breathing is

_____

5. (a) Pangs are
   (b) Grapples are
   (c) claws used for grasping.
   (d) playful remarks.

_____

6. (a) To decelerate is to
   (b) To banter is to
   (c) move at a slow, steady pace.
   (d) reduce speed.

_____

adept

audible

azure

banter

capacious

copious

crucial

decelerate

deploy

facilitate

fastidious

fitful

grapple

pang

precede

7. (a) that is put in writing.   (c) A crucial statement is one
   (b) that is vitally important.   (d) An audible statement is one

8. (a) To precede something   (c) To deploy something
   (b) is to get rid of it.   (d) is to come before it.

9. (a) An azure bowl is   (c) one that holds a lot.
   (b) A capacious bowl is   (d) one that is filled to the brim.

10. (a) have no further use for them.   (c) To banter with people is to
   (b) use them where they are needed.   (d) To deploy people is to

8B Just the Right Word

Improve each of the following sentences by crossing out the bold phrase and replacing it with a word (or a form of the word) from Word List 8.

1. Standing before the students gathered in the auditorium, Ms. Benton was barely **able to be heard** until someone gave her a microphone.

2. The catcher and the umpire **exchanged lighthearted comments** as the batter walked up to the plate.

3. New York City is still **trying very hard to deal** with the problem of homelessness.

4. Leaving the museum around two in the afternoon, Judy and George were reminded by the **sudden sharp twinges** of hunger that they hadn't eaten since breakfast.

5. My cousin Luis was **very skillful** at getting the basketball in the net.

6. The manager is so **hard to please** that even the salt and pepper shakers must be placed just so.

7. Fluffy white clouds stood out against the **clear blue of the** sky.

8. When the president visited our city, the police chief **put into use** an additional forty police officers.

9. A cardinal **comes in rank before** a bishop in the Catholic church.

10. Eleanor's driving instructor told her to apply the brakes gently to **cause the vehicle to slow down**.

8C Applying Meanings

Circle the letter of each correct answer to the questions below. Questions may have more than one correct answer.

1. Which of the following might cause **pangs**?
   - (a) hunger
   - (b) fatigue
   - (c) fear
   - (d) serenity

2. Which of the following might cause a vehicle to **decelerate**?
   - (a) applying the brake
   - (b) shifting to a lower gear
   - (c) stepping on the gas
   - (d) going down a hill

3. Which of the following might be **azure**?
   - (a) a jug
   - (b) the sky
   - (c) a ceiling
   - (d) a leaf

4. Which of the following would you expect to be **adept**?
   - (a) a diamond cutter
   - (b) a fledgling water skier
   - (c) an airline pilot
   - (d) a major league pitcher

5. Which of the following might be **deployed**?
   - (a) tanks
   - (b) soldiers
   - (c) moonlight
   - (d) ships

6. Which of the following might be said by a **fastidious** person?
   - (a) "Do whatever you think."
   - (b) "This towel is not soft enough."
   - (c) "Try to get it right the first time."
   - (d) "Did you vacuum under the sofa?"

7. Which of the following might one **grapple** with?
   - (a) an opponent
   - (b) an anthology
   - (c) a problem
   - (d) a pseudonym

8. Which of the following is **crucial** to learning?
   - (a) a high school diploma
   - (b) smaller classes
   - (c) computers
   - (d) a desire to understand

adept
audible
azure
banter
capacious
copious
crucial
decelerate
deploy
facilitate
fastidious
fitful
grapple
pang
precede

8D Word Study

Complete the analogies by selecting the pair of words whose relationship most resembles the relationship of the pair in capital letters. Circle the letter in front of the pair you choose.

1. AZURE : SKY ::
   (a) wet : water
   (b) cloudy : rain
   (c) sweet : sugar
   (d) green : grass

2. AUDIBLE : EAR ::
   (a) visible : eye
   (b) flexible : hand
   (c) spoken : voice
   (d) loud : music

3. ADEPT : SKILLFUL ::
   (a) profound : shallow
   (b) copious : scarce
   (c) prudent : careless
   (d) crucial : vital

4. TRICKLE : DELUGE ::
   (a) bruise : abrasion
   (b) proprietor : store
   (c) parent : generation
   (d) scarcity : profusion

5. BRUSQUE : BRUSQUENESS ::
   (a) reclusive : profusion
   (b) simulated : simulation
   (c) foolish : inanity
   (d) angry : tirade

6. COLLEAGUE : WORK ::
   (a) fledgling : wing
   (b) fanfare : trumpet
   (c) mettle : metal
   (d) friend : play

7. ANARCHY : LAW ::
   (a) tyranny : freedom
   (b) inkling : suspicion
   (c) calamity : misfortune
   (d) mutiny : ship

8. GRAPPLE : CLAW ::
   (a) dispel : smoke
   (b) shackle : prisoner
   (c) chop : axe
   (d) decelerate : speed

9. WARM : SWELTERING ::
   (a) wet : rainy
   (b) chilly : freezing
   (c) sunny : cloudy
   (d) snowy : wintry

10. FLEDGLING : FLY ::
    (a) toddler : walk
    (b) banter : tease
    (c) baby : cry
    (d) replica : simulate

8E Passage

Read the passage below; then complete the exercise that follows.

Women in Space, Part Two

On June 18, 1983, the space shuttle *Challenger* rose from the launch pad to begin a five-day mission. Astronaut Sally Ride, the flight engineer, was not the first woman in space. Two Soviet female cosmonauts had **preceded** her; but she was making history as the first American woman to make such a flight.

The thunderous roar of the rockets filled her headphones, and a **pang** of fear gripped her as she wondered if everything was working properly. The feeling quickly passed, and in less than ten minutes *Challenger* was in orbit, floating almost two hundred miles above Earth. The only sound was the barely **audible** hum of the fans circulating the air. Outside, the sky was jet black; with no air at this altitude to scatter the sunlight, the sky had lost its familiar **azure** hue.

Released from the harnesses that held them in place, the five crew members floated weightlessly in zero gravity, a novel experience for all but the shuttle commander, Bob Crippen, who was the only crew member to have flown in space before. As the astronauts relaxed, **bantering** among themselves, Dr. Ride informed ground control that they had "three turkeys and two hams" aboard, although she did not reveal their identities.

Because the shuttle orbited Earth every ninety minutes, the sun rose and set sixteen times every twenty-four hours; night and day, therefore, had little meaning for the five astronauts. During her first rest period, Dr. Ride slept **fitfully**, but soon she adjusted to the routine aboard the shuttle. She once admitted that she was not a **fastidious** housekeeper, but since the cramped space of the shuttle's living quarters made neatness important, she was careful to stow away everything she did not have an immediate need for. Eating in space was no problem. Of course the astronauts didn't sprinkle salt on their food; it would just float away. Disposing of bodily waste—a subject that had intrigued reporters—was **facilitated** by using an air suction device in the toilet.

The **capacious** cargo bay was located behind the crew's living quarters. On this particular mission it held two large communication satellites, known as comsats, as well as a $23 million orbiting laboratory designed to carry out various experiments while separated from the shuttle. In addition to her duties as the flight engineer, responsible for checking the workings of the spacecraft, Dr. Ride was also in charge of **deploying** the orbiting laboratory once the two comsats had been released.

One of Dr. Ride's qualifications for this mission had been that she was especially **adept** at handling the robot arm, a jointed fifty-foot pole with a **grapple** at the end, operated by remote control from the shuttle's flight deck. She used the robot arm to remove the orbiting laboratory from the cargo bay and to release it so that it could float freely away from the shuttle. From a distance of one thousand feet, a camera in the orbiting laboratory took spectacular photographs of the shuttle that were beamed to Earth and shown on television. At the conclusion of the experiments, the shuttle moved closer to the orbiting laboratory, which Dr. Ride recovered and tucked away in the cargo bay, again using the robot arm.

With their work completed and the flight nearing its end, the shuttle's five crew members prepared to return to Earth. Because their bodies had lost fluids to adjust to weightlessness, they drank **copious** amounts of water. In addition, they put away everything that had been floating freely in the cabin. Once within Earth's gravity, these objects would crash to the floor.

The astronauts knew that reentering Earth's atmosphere at just the right angle was **crucial** for a successful landing. During reentry, the shuttle needed to **decelerate** sharply. The friction caused by air resistance would heat up its exterior to over 2,500 degrees Fahrenheit, but the

adept
audible
azure
banter
capacious
copious
crucial
decelerate
deploy
facilitate
fastidious
fitful
grapple
pang
precede

special heat tiles on the outside would prevent the shuttle from burning up and would keep the interior comfortable.

All went well at the conclusion of Space Transportation System—Flight 7; after a ninety-eight-orbit flight of two and a half million miles, *Challenger* landed safely at Edwards Air Force Base in California. One of the banners that greeted Dr. Ride as she emerged read "HERSTORY MADE TODAY BY SALLY RIDE."

Answer each of the following questions in the form of a sentence. If a question does not contain a vocabulary word from this lesson's word list, use one in your answer. Use each word only once. Questions and answers will then contain all fifteen words (or forms of the words).

1. How does the sky change as one gets above Earth's atmosphere?

2. Why would it be inaccurate to describe the shuttle living quarters as **capacious**?

3. In what ways do you think the lack of gravity **facilitated** the astronauts' work on the space ship?

4. How was Dr. Ride's sleep affected when she first went into orbit?

5. What is the meaning of **grapple** as it is used in the passage?

6. What task **preceded** the release of the orbiting laboratory?

7. Do you think crew members are likely to **banter** as they board the space shuttle? Explain your answer.

8. What did Dr. Ride hear as the *Challenger* lifted off?

9. Why did the astronauts need to be **fastidious** about putting everything away before reentry?

10. What would happen if the shuttle failed to **decelerate** on reentry?

11. Why is a plentiful supply of drinking water required on a shuttle mission?

12. What is the meaning of **deploy** as it is used in the passage?

13. What **crucial** role did the heat tiles on the outside of the shuttle play?

14. In what way must the pilot be **adept** during the return to Earth?

15. Why might the astronauts feel a **pang** of regret upon returning to Earth?

FUN & FASCINATING FACTS

During the Middle Ages much time and energy was devoted to trying to turn common metals, such as iron or lead, into precious metals, like gold and silver. The study of this subject was known as alchemy. A person who had acquired knowledge of how to bring about such miraculous change was known as an **adept**. In time, the word was extended to include anyone who was highly skilled in an activity. Then later it came into more common use as an adjective, meaning "highly skilled."

The antonym of *adept* is *inept*, which means "clumsy" or "awkward." (Celina apologized for her *inept* introduction of Chad's father as his grandfather.)

In Lesson 1 you learned that *excruciating* comes from the Latin *crux*, which means "a cross." Although the connection is not as clear, the adjective **crucial** is formed from the same Latin root. The explanation lies in the fact that the Romans used crosses not just as a means of execution but also as signposts. If a traveler came to a fork in the road, it was extremely important, or *crucial*, to take the correct road; the cross placed there as a signpost guided the traveler in the right direction.

Review for Lessons 5–8

Hidden Message In the boxes provided write the words from Lessons 5 through 8 that are missing in each of the sentences below. The number following each sentence gives the word list from which the missing word is taken. When the exercise is finished, the shaded boxes will spell out a short poem by American humorist Ogden Nash (1902-1971).*

1. A _____ inspection revealed no flaws. (6)

2. The ballplayer wouldn't _____ to acknowledge the hecklers in the stands. (7)

3. Jesse had no _____ of what he intended to do. (5)

4. I joined in my classmates' playful _____ . (8)

5. The police will _____ the suspects. (6)

6. The sailors who took part in the _____ were punished. (5)

7. The _____ had hooked onto a large object on the seabed. (8)

8. I'll plead "not guilty" when they _____ me on Monday. (6)

9. The _____ company grew rapidly at first. (7)

10. Telling the truth will _____ these rumors. (7)

11. A _____ appearance is not appropriate at work. (5)

12. Dr. Ransom is a _____ of Dr. Sanchez. (7)

13. I am _____ by such arrogant remarks. (5)

14. I took _____ notes at the lecture. (8)

15. She _____ with her friends to play the practical joke. (6)

16. My mind was filled with a _____ of ideas. (5)

17. Professional painters are very _____ workers. (8)

18. Without any laws, we would have _____ . (6)

19. Sal was suspected of _____ items from the office. (5)

20. _____ jokes are rarely funny. (7)

21. You'll _____ in July without air-conditioning. (6)

22. Today we _____ on a vast new project. (5)

23. Sometimes it's _____ to get a second medical opinion. (5)

24. The movie _____ life in a small midwestern town. (5)

25. Pat's _____ behavior shocked the class. (5)

26. Apply the brake so that the car will _____ . (8)

27. The new computerized system will _____ filling orders. (8)

28. Her _____ manner had a calming effect on us. (5)

29. The negotiations were _____ over a year. (7)

30. Mr. Cass threatened to _____ our waterguns. (5)

31. The team's _____ was tested by the Bears. (7)

32. The debate made very clear the _____ between the candidates. (6)

33. This is a(n) _____ of an ancient Korean vase. (7)

34. Don't let your opponent's size _____ you. (7)

35. The time of departure is _____ on the weather. (7)

36. I meant to send a thank-you note before so much time had _____ . (6)

37. I need more time to _____ all this information. (6)

38. Why we _____ sports figures baffles me. (6)

39. His _____ behavior made us question his sanity. (6)

40. I had to _____ them for their bad manners. (5)

41. It is _____ that you attend the meeting. (8)

42. The cost of adding an extra coat of paint to the small room is _____ . (7)

43. The _____ washed away parts of the road. (7)

44. Progress was _____ at first but soon became steady. (8)

45. The flooding was an unforeseen _____ . (6)

46. Can we _____ two guards at the front door? (8)

47. A _____ trunk held all our belongings. (8)

48. The police did not _____ the thief yet. (6)

49. The letters ABC _____ DEF in the alphabet. (8)

50. When the music began, the president's arrival seemed _____ . (6)

51. A _____ person will not tolerate sloppy work. (8)

Lesson 9

> ## Word List
Study the definitions of the words below; then do the exercises for the lesson.

abet
ə bet´

v. To encourage or assist in some activity, especially a questionable one.
Randy **abetted** his friend in stealing pumpkins by helping him to lug them home.

agile
aj´ əl

adj. 1. Able to move quickly and easily; nimble.
Alexandra's **agile** steps followed Wilfredo's as the band played a tango.
2. Able to think quickly.
In the final round of the chess tournament, Gary Kasparov's **agile** mind enabled him to think five moves ahead.
agility *n.* (ə jil´ ə tē) Quickness of mind or body.
Our karate instructor carefully developed our **agility** through repeated practice of the basic movements.

allot
ə lät´

v. To assign or distribute as a portion or share.
Ms. Kaplan usually **allotted** fifteen minutes at the beginning of each French class for conversation practice.

balmy
bäm´ ē

adj. Soothing, mild.
Instead of the **balmy** Florida weather she had expected, Cynthia experienced cold, rainy days for most of her vacation.

congregate
käŋ´ grə gāt

v. To come together in a group, assemble.
After the war ended in Europe, thousands of people **congregated** in refugee camps, waiting for help.

divert
də vʉrt´

v. 1. To turn aside.
By sandbagging the shore, we can **divert** some of the flood waters.
2. To entertain or amuse.
A juggler **diverted** the audience during the scene changes.
diversion *n.* 1. The act of turning from a course or concern.
A flat tire on our trip to Ohio in the middle of a snowstorm was a **diversion** we had not anticipated.
2. Something that amuses or entertains.
Collecting shells of so many colors and sizes was a **diversion** our whole family enjoyed on our visit to Puerto Rico.

humdrum
hum´ drum

adj. Lacking excitement; boring or monotonous.
Bagging groceries is a **humdrum** job, but the flexible hours allow me to finish school.

influx
in´ fluks

n. A flowing or pouring in; arrival in massive numbers.
Hotel owners hope that this winter's coastal oil spill will not affect the **influx** of summer tourists.

intricate
in´ tri kət

adj. Complicated; having many related details or parts.
Susan's paper for art history described the **intricate** arrangement of colors in the old textile.

memento mə men′ tō	*n.* Something kept as a reminder of a past event; a souvenir. Madelaine kept the sand dollar as a **memento** of her day at the New Jersey shore.
query kwir′ ē	*n.* A question. Naomi's job with the airline was to answer all **queries** about delayed planes. *v.* To ask or ask about. Doctor Feldman **queried** Bruce about his childhood diseases.
sporadic spə rad′ ik	*adj.* Happening occasionally; not regularly. Last summer, between **sporadic** acting jobs, we worked as waiters or cabdrivers.
staple stā′ pəl	*n.* 1. A basic food that is used frequently and in large amounts. Rice and beans are **staples** in many Caribbean households. 2. A U-shaped fastener with sharp ends. Remove the **staples** before you put those papers through the copy machine. *v.* To attach with staples. After the students finished writing their reports, they **stapled** the pages together. *adj.* Most important, principal. Wheat and corn are **staple** crops of Canada.
tumult tōō′ mult	*n.* Noisy excitement; an uproar or disturbance. Entering the house through the chimney, the squirrel caused a **tumult** until my sister finally caught it and released it in the backyard. **tumultuous** *adj.* Marked by uproar or excitement, turbulent. A **tumultuous** crowd waited at the airport to greet the triumphant Mexican soccer team.
unseemly un sēm′ lē	*adj.* Not suitable; inappropriate or improper. Sharon and Richard began an **unseemly** argument at the wedding dinner of their daughter.

9A Finding Meanings

Choose two phrases to form a sentence that correctly uses a word from Word List 9. Write each sentence in the space provided.

1. (a) to distribute them.   (c) To divert funds is
   (b) to account fully for them.   (d) To allot funds is

2. (a) A staple is   (c) A memento is
   (b) a basic food.   (d) a short note.

3. (a) Tumult is   (c) quickness of mind or body.
   (b) Agility is   (d) a feeling of unreasonable panic.

4. (a) An influx is something
   (b) A memento is something
   (c) kept as a reminder of a past event.
   (d) that is inappropriate and out of place.

5. (a) A humdrum task
   (b) An intricate task
   (c) is one that is quickly completed.
   (d) is one that lacks interest or excitement.

6. (a) question closely.
   (b) To congregate is to
   (c) entertain or amuse.
   (d) To divert is to

7. (a) A query is
   (b) An influx is
   (c) movement into a place.
   (d) a turning point.

8. (a) An unseemly proposal is one
   (b) that is very detailed.
   (c) that is concisely written.
   (d) An intricate proposal is one

9. (a) be suspicious of that person.
   (b) give support to that person.
   (c) To abet someone is to
   (d) To query someone is to

10. (a) is one filled with noisy excitement.
    (b) is one that is boring.
    (c) A balmy day
    (d) A tumultuous day

abet

agile

allot

balmy

congregate

divert

humdrum

influx

intricate

memento

query

sporadic

staple

tumult

unseemly

9B Just the Right Word

Improve each of the following sentences by crossing out the bold phrase and replacing it with a word (or a form of the word) from Word List 9.

1. Rain was **coming down from time to time** all through the day we had chosen for painting the house.

2. Beautiful beaches and impressive rain forests have helped make tourism a **very important** industry in Hawaii.

3. Barbara's attention was **turned away** from the violinist's solo by the commotion going on two rows behind her.

4. Anyone who wishes to be a gymnast must learn to be **able to move quickly and easily**.

5. The campers were **assigned as their portion** one dish of ice cream at the evening square dance.

6. Mom made us spit out our gum before the memorial service because chewing it, she said, would be most **unsuitable for such an occasion.**

7. A **warm and gentle** breeze from the ocean helped keep us cool on a sweltering August afternoon.

8. The immigration officer **asked a number of questions of** Jonas about U.S. history and government during his citizenship interview.

9. The announcement of the verdict caused **great excitement and confusion** in the press room.

10. Last year scientists predicted the **continuous pouring in** of killer bees from South to North America, but it never took place.

9C Applying Meanings

Circle the letter of each correct answer to the questions below. Questions may have more than one correct answer.

1. Which of the following might be considered a **diversion?**
   (a) doing homework
   (b) getting stuck in traffic
   (c) watching television
   (d) playing softball

2. Which of the following could be **intricate?**
   (a) a drawing
   (b) a plan
   (c) the plot of a movie
   (d) a grimace

3. Which of the following are **staples?**
   (a) beans
   (b) rice
   (c) ice cubes
   (d) cookies

4. Which of the following needs to be **agile?**
   (a) an Olympic skater
   (b) a downhill skier
   (c) an artist's model
   (d) a hockey goalie

5. Which of the following is a **query?**
   (a) "Feeling better?"
   (b) "What's the matter?"
   (c) "Let's go."
   (d) "How do you open this?"

6. Which of the following can **congregate**?
   - (a) people
   - (b) animals
   - (c) plants
   - (d) birds

7. Which of the following could be **humdrum**?
   - (a) a job
   - (b) a movie
   - (c) a calamity
   - (d) a mutiny

8. Which of the following might be **tumultuous**?
   - (a) a sleeping infant
   - (b) an election
   - (c) a parade
   - (d) a fireplace

9D Word Study

Choose from the two words provided and use each word only once when filling in the spaces. One space should be left blank.

intricate/complicated

1. The wallpaper has a(n) _____ pattern of intertwined branches and birds.

2. The math equations were more _____ than the freshmen expected.

3. 18,074,030 is an extremely _____ number.

sporadic/occasional

4. The _____ weather patterns make it difficult for forecasters to make predictions.

5. Even though Malcolm is trying to cut down on caffeine, he enjoys a(n) _____ cup of tea.

6. Emily's visits were _____ and then stopped altogether.

fitful/irregular

7. The doctor was concerned about the patient's _____ heartbeat.

8. After a(n) _____ sleep, Leonard could barely drag himself out of bed.

9. The waves grew increasingly _____ as the hurricane neared the coast.

replica/copy

10. A _____ of twelve inches would be a foot.

11. The bank needs a _____ of your signature for its records.

12. The *Mayflower* docked in Plymouth, Massachusetts, is a _____ of the Pilgrims' ship.

abet

agile

allot

balmy

congregate

divert

humdrum

influx

intricate

memento

query

sporadic

staple

tumult

unseemly

assimilate/absorb

13. A sponge can _____ six times its weight in water.

14. Katy seemed unable to _____ the meaning of the word "no."

15. The brain has to _____ sensory information from many different sources.

9E Passage

Read the passage below; then complete the exercise that follows.

The Children of the *Bounty*

Many people dream of living on a remote tropical island where there are no cars and no crime. For the people of Pitcairn Island, this dream is their reality. Until 1789, Pitcairn was uninhabited. In that year, Fletcher Christian, together with eight other mutineers from the *Bounty* and eighteen Tahitians, arrived at and settled on this tiny island in the South Pacific. By the late 1800s the island's population had grown to over two hundred. Today, the number has dwindled to fewer than fifty. However, the island's governing council is not greatly concerned about the declining population. It receives thousands of **queries** from people all over the world who would like to live there. Nevertheless, it rarely issues the official entry document called "Licence to Land" because Pitcairners have no wish to be swamped by an **influx** of new residents.

Life on Pitcairn is easygoing. The inhabitants enjoy **balmy** weather all year round and the island has plenty of water. Sweet potatoes, melons, bananas, and coffee are among the crops grown in its fertile soil. The older inhabitants spend most of their time fishing, growing vegetables, and making wooden carvings and woven baskets.

Because life changes little from day to day, visits from ships passing by on their way from the Panama Canal to New Zealand are eagerly awaited. The island's steep cliffs and lack of harbors make it impossible for ships to come to land, so they must anchor about a mile offshore. Islanders **congregate** at the town landing in Adamstown, the island's only town, when a ship arrives to watch the launching of the forty-foot longboat that goes out to meet it to replenish supplies and to sell **mementos**. During rough weather, when the boat is pitching wildly, those on board have a formidable task getting from the longboat to the deck of the ship by rope ladder. Only the most **agile** attempt it.

The crews on these passing ships are eager to buy the carvings and baskets made by the islanders. An **intricately** carved replica of the *Bounty*, a popular item, can sell for several hundred dollars or more, depending on the skill of the carver. The ships' visits are **sporadic**, with weeks or even months going by without one. For this reason, the Pitcairners take advantage of these visits to trade fish, fruits, and vegetables for canned goods and **staples**, such as flour and sugar, that they cannot provide for themselves. Everything obtained from passing ships is **allotted** equally among the island's families. In this way, no one lacks the necessities.

This tropical paradise, however, is not for everyone. Young people often feel frustrated by the lack of opportunity. Many of them wish to exchange what they regard as the **humdrum** existence on the island for what they believe will be more exciting lives in the outside world. Not only do they find limitations in jobs unappealing, but they also complain that life on Pitcairn offers few **diversions**. Dancing is forbidden and there is no television. Any display of affection, such as holding hands in public, is regarded as **unseemly** by the island's ruling council, which has passed laws banning such behavior. While many young people leave, some return later, unable to cope with the **tumult** of the modern world.

Pitcairn, a volcanic speck of rock less than two square miles in area and inhabited by only nine families, has a fascination for the outside world out of all proportion to its size. It has been the subject of no fewer than 2,500 books and articles. One reason, of course, is obvious—its dramatic past, a past that began on an April morning in 1789 when Captain Bligh was rudely awakened to discover that Fletcher Christian, **abetted** by mutinous crew members, had seized control of the *Bounty*.

Answer each of the following questions in the form of a sentence. If a question does not contain a vocabulary word from this lesson's word list, use one in your answer. Use each word only once. Questions and answers will then contain all fifteen words (or forms of the words).

1. Why are there no heating bills on Pitcairn?

2. Why hasn't there been an **influx** of tourists to Pitcairn?

3. What is the meaning of **staples** as it is used in the passage?

4. Why do you suppose the ships' visits are **sporadic**?

5. Name two activities that Pitcairn teenagers might find **humdrum**.

6. In what ways might teenagers from Pitcairn Island find life in a U. S. city **tumultuous**?

7. According to the passage, what is the content of a lot of the mail sent to Pitcairn?

8. How do the islanders make sure no one lacks necessary food?

9. What is the meaning of **diversions** as it is used in the passage?

10. Why is it inaccurate to say that few Pitcairners are interested in a ship's arrival?

11. Why is showing affection in public banned by Pitcairn's governing council?

12. Why is a carving of the *Bounty* considered a suitable **memento** of Pitcairn?

13. What do you think determines the price of an **intricately** carved model of the *Bounty?*

14. How many of those who originally sailed to Pitcairn with Christian had helped him with the mutiny?

15. Why would it be inaccurate to say that any of the islanders could be sent out on the longboat to board the ship?

FUN & FASCINATING FACTS

We usually use the adjective **balmy** to refer to conditions of climate or weather (a *balmy* day; a *balmy* breeze). But *balmy* has a secondary, slang meaning of, "odd or peculiar in behavior." An alternative spelling for this meaning is *barmy,* which has an interesting origin. *Barm* is the yeasty foam that rises to the top of certain alcoholic beverages as they are being brewed. A connection was made between this activity and odd or peculiar behavior. A person acting strangely was described as *barmy.* Confusion then occurred between two quite separate and distinct words. The result is that a person acting oddly can be described as *balmy* or *barmy.* A gentle breeze, however, can only be *balmy,* not *barmy.*

The Latin verb *fluere* means "to flow" and forms the root of **influx,** "a flowing or pouring in." Other words formed from this root include: *fluid,* "any substance that flows"; *fluent,* "able to write or speak in a flowing, easy way"; *fluctuate,* "to move back and forth or up and down in a wavelike or flowing manner"; *flux,* "a flowing movement," also "a state of constant change"; and *confluence,* "a flowing together, as of two streams or rivers."

Lesson 10

Word List

Study the definitions of the words below; then do the exercises for the lesson.

abject
ab´ jekt

adj. 1. Most miserable; wretched.
King Lear's life changed from one of luxury and power to one of **abject** poverty and helplessness.

advocate
ad´ və kāt

v. To plead in favor of; to defend.
This organization **advocates** the release of all people imprisoned for their beliefs.
n. (ad´ və kət) One who argues for or defends a person, group, or idea.
Former Surgeon General Koop was a strong **advocate** for a ban on cigarette advertising.

atrocity
ə träs´ ə tē

n. An act of great cruelty and wickedness.
The war crimes judges in The Hague examined **atrocities** committed during the war in the former Yugoslavia.
atrocious *adj.* (ə trō´ shəs) 1. Very brutal, wicked, or cruel.
The Nazis carried out **atrocious** medical experiments on their prisoners.
2. Appallingly bad; outrageous.
The owners of the kennel were prosecuted after reporters revealed that the animals lived under **atrocious** conditions.

commemorate
kə mem´ ə rāt

v. To serve as a memorial to; to remember in a solemn manner.
The tablet on the front of the house **commemorates** its importance as a station on the Underground Railroad.

dialect
dī´ ə lekt

n. A form of a language spoken in a certain geographical region that has its own grammar, pronunciation, and vocabulary.
A Spanish-speaking person from Madrid might not completely understand a **dialect** spoken in Cuba.

dire
dīr

adj. Having terrible consequences; urgent or desperate.
Pol Pot's reign in Cambodia, which began in 1975, had a **dire** effect on the lives of most Cambodians.

elite
e lēt´

n. A group that enjoys superior status to others.
Many of Edith Wharton's novels are set in the homes of the social **elite** of New York City during the 1890s.
adj. Considered superior to others.
In the 1800s, girls working in the textile mills sent their earnings home to help pay for the education of their brothers, who often attended **elite** universities.

enhance
en hans´

v. To make greater or better.
The greenhouse window in our new kitchen **enhances** the room's light, airy feeling.

flagrant
flā´ grənt

adj. Clearly offensive or bad; conspicuously acting against what is right.
Trying to conceal the Watergate break-in was a **flagrant** abuse of presidential power.

languish
laṇ´ gwish

v. To lose hope, strength, or vitality because of neglect or bad conditions.
We **languished** on the porch, our tennis rackets at our feet, as the rain soaked everything.

mute
myo͞ot

v. To soften or tone down the sound of.
The state legislature has agreed to build walls at the edge of the airport to **mute** the roar of the jet engines for nearby residents.
adj. Not speaking or not able to speak; silent.
Julie remained **mute** when the customs officer asked her name.

raze
rāz

v. To level to the ground; to destroy completely.
Just as the row of seventeenth-century buildings was about to be **razed**, the preservation society requested a delay.

reprisal
ri prī´ zəl

n. A retaliation for an injury.
The rocket attack came as a swift and deadly **reprisal** for the bombing of the embassy.

turmoil
tʉr´ moil

n. A state of confusion or agitation; tumult.
With flood waters rising and an order to evacuate our home in an hour, my family was in a **turmoil**, trying to decide what to do first.

wreak
rēk

v. 1. To bring about or inflict.
The tornado **wreaked** destruction and death along the path it followed through the center of town.
2. To express or vent.
Sidney **wreaked** his anger by pounding on the hood of the ruined car.

10A Finding Meanings

Choose two phrases to form a sentence that correctly uses a word from Word List 10. Write each sentence in the space provided.

1. (a) To enhance a building's appearance
   (b) To raze a building
   (c) is to destroy it completely.
   (d) is to have control over it.

2. (a) an act of retaliation for an injury.
   (b) a way of remembering a past event.
   (c) A dialect is
   (d) A reprisal is

3. (a) A mute victim is
   (b) An abject victim is
   (c) one whose state is pitiable.
   (d) one who protests vigorously.

4. (a) A flagrant action is
   (b) A dire action is
   (c) one that matters little.
   (d) one that has serious consequences.

5. (a) a distinct form of a language.   (c) An atrocity is
   (b) a celebration to honor a past event. (d) A dialect is

6. (a) A flagrant attack   (c) is one made secretly.
   (b) is one made in silence.   (d) A mute protest

7. (a) is to be in a weakened state.   (c) is to be at peace with oneself.
   (b) To be in turmoil   (d) To languish

8. (a) An atrocity is   (c) An elite is
   (b) an act of appalling cruelty.   (d) a display of agility.

9. (a) To commemorate something is to (c) improve it.
   (b) To enhance something is to   (d) cause it to fail.

10. (a) a group considered superior to others. (c) An elite is
    (b) a victim of an unprovoked attack.   (d) An advocate is

abject
advocate
atrocity
commemorate
dialect
dire
elite
enhance
flagrant
languish
mute
raze
reprisal
turmoil
wreak

10B Just the Right Word

Improve each of the following sentences by crossing out the bold phrase and replacing it with a word (or a form of the word) from Word List 10.

1. **Brutal and wicked** acts were committed by both sides in the civil war.

2. The pine forest's thick bed of needles completely **absorbed the sounds of** our footsteps.

3. This drought has left all of the crops, but especially the corn, **losing strength and vitality** in the fields.

4. The French auto mechanic who towed our rented car to his garage spoke in a **form of the language** that we did not understand.

5. Those who died during the fighting at Gettysburg have been **remembered in a fittingly solemn manner** by Lincoln's concise and eloquent speech.

6. Olivia's rudeness to the coach was so **clearly offensive** that her teammates thought she would be dropped from the team.

7. On the morning of my sister's wedding, our house was in a **confused and agitated state**, with food, flowers, and relatives all arriving at once.

8. A bulldozer was brought in to **completely destroy** the abandoned building.

9. Convinced of the devastating effects of cigarette smoking on health, many Americans **argue in favor of** a very high tax on tobacco products.

10. Brought on by a series of unusually heavy snowfalls, the **extremely urgent and desperate** conditions were hardest on North Dakotan farmers with livestock.

10C Applying Meanings

Circle the letter of each correct answer to the questions below. Questions may have more than one correct answer.

1. Which of the following can be **wreaked**?
   (a) audacity
   (b) prudence
   (c) anger
   (d) destruction

2. Which of the following might a conscientious **advocate** do?
   (a) organize meetings
   (b) become reclusive
   (c) make speeches
   (d) write letters

3. Which of the following would **mute** sounds?
   (a) a loudspeaker
   (b) a thick wall
   (c) a hearing aid
   (d) earmuffs

4. Which of the following nouns might correctly be modified by **abject**?
   (a) misery
   (b) poverty
   (c) serenity
   (d) despair

5. Which of the following could be **commemorated**?
   (a) a victory
   (b) a defeat
   (c) a discovery
   (d) a grimace

6. Which of the following can be **razed**?
   (a) children
   (b) rivers
   (c) buildings
   (d) villages

7. Which of the following might describe members of an **elite** law firm?

(a) unemployed   (c) wealthy

(b) claustrophobic   (d) powerful

8. Which of the following would be considered a **flagrant** act?

(a) threatening someone's life   (c) burning the flag

(b) saving someone's life   (d) leading a mutiny

10D Word Study

In this exercise, you are going to build ten words. You do this by combining the correct prefix with a root formed from a Latin word. The materials you will use are listed below:

Use these prefixes:

ab- (from)   *inter-* (between)

ad-, ap-, as- (to; toward)   *pre-* (before)

com-, con- (together)   *pro-* (out)

Combine the correct prefixes with roots formed from these Latin words:

cedere (to go)   *rogare* (to ask)

gregare (to assemble)   *similis* (like; similar)

jacere (to throw)   *spirare* (to breathe)

memorare (to remind)   *trahere* (to draw or drag)

prehendare (to grasp)   *vocare* (to speak)

Use each clue to guide you to the correct answer. Write the word in the space provided. All ten words are taken from this or an earlier lesson. The number in parentheses gives the lesson from which each word is taken.

abject

advocate

atrocity

commemorate

dialect

dire

elite

enhance

flagrant

languish

mute

raze

reprisal

turmoil

wreak

1. When these people meet, they put their heads so close together, they practically breathe each other's air. The word is _____. (6)

2. The family moved to a new country and learned the customs and traditions. The word is _____. (6)

3. Who or what goes before the others? The word is _____. (8)

4. The detective handcuffed the criminal. The word is _____. (6)

5. People's fortunes sunk during the Great Depression, leaving many in poverty. The word for their misfortune is _____. (10)

6. Police ask witnesses many questions to reconstruct a crime. The word is _____. (6)

7. During opening and closing arguments, the lawyers speak to the jury about the guilt or innocence of the defendant. The word is _____. (10)

8. It may be a long, drawn-out process. If so, the word is _____. (7)

9. When people assemble or come together, the word is _____. (9)

10. One way of bringing people together is to remind them of someone or some event that seems worth remembering. The word is _____. (10)

10E Passage

Read the passage below; then complete the exercise that follows.

Rigoberta Menchu

The four-hundredth anniversary of Columbus's famous voyage was **commemorated** in 1892 with much fanfare throughout North and South America. The five-hundredth anniversary celebrations, in 1992, were **muted** by comparison, as many people drew attention to how thoroughly the European settlers had **wreaked** devastation upon the original inhabitants of the Americas. In that year, too, the Nobel Committee awarded its Peace Prize to Rigoberta Menchu, a thirty-three-year-old native woman from Guatemala, for her "increasingly prominent part as an **advocate** of native rights." The head of the committee, in announcing the award, stated that it had been deliberately timed to coincide with the five-hundredth anniversary of Columbus's voyage.

Until Menchu was sixteen, she spoke only Quiché, one of some twenty **dialects** of the Guatemalan native peoples. The Quiché are the descendants of the once-proud Mayas, whose civilization flourished in Central America until about A.D. 900. Menchu came to prominence in 1983 with the publication in Spanish of her autobiography *I, Rigoberta Menchu*, which gives an account of the **atrocities** committed by government forces from the 1960s up to the 1980s against the peasant population of Guatemala.

While the country's **elite** lived in heavily guarded, luxurious homes in Guatemala City, the native peoples, who made up more than half of the population, lived in **abject** poverty. Their little plots of land, which provided only a meager living, could be seized without warning by wealthy landowners. To protest was to risk severe punishment by the army, whose methods included the **razing** of entire villages along with the slaughter of their inhabitants. During the thirty-year conflict, an estimated one hundred thousand unarmed native peasants were killed, and tens of thousands fled the **turmoil** in the countryside for the safety of neighboring Mexico. There they **languished** for many years in refugee camps. Others escaped to the mountains to wage a decades-long civil war against the army.

Menchu's own family experienced terrible losses for resisting the army's rigid control of the country. Her father was repeatedly beaten, tortured, and jailed for organizing nonviolent protests. He was part of a group that occupied the Spanish embassy in Guatemala City in order to draw attention to the government's **flagrant** abuses of human rights. During this occupation, the building was deliberately set on fire, killing those trapped inside. Later, Menchu's sixteen-year-old brother, along with twenty others, was abducted and killed by the military. A year later her mother was abducted by army officers and tortured before being tied to a tree until she died. Her body was left unburied and visible as a **dire** warning to other "troublemakers."

Two of Menchu's sisters joined the armed resistance groups fighting within the country. She herself escaped to Mexico in 1981. From there she worked to draw the world's attention to the plight of her people. The awarding of the Nobel Peace Prize **enhanced** enormously her ability to tell her story, both within Guatemala and in the world at large. She used the $1.2 million prize money to further her campaign for peace in Guatemala and the rights of native people throughout the hemisphere. There was one further benefit of winning the prize: as a world-famous figure, she was free to visit her native land without fear of **reprisal** by government forces.

The thirty years of civil war ended in 1996 with the signing of peace accords between the rebels and the government. Progress toward the goals outlined in the accords was painfully slow, largely because of the mistrust that still existed between the two sides. In February of 2004, President Oscar Berger appointed what he called "a goodwill ambassador" to speed up the process. The person he named to the post was Rigoberta Menchu.

Answer each of the following questions in the form of a sentence. If a question does not contain a vocabulary word from this lesson's word list, use one in your answer. Use each word only once. Questions and answers will then contain all fifteen words (or forms of the words).

1. How do you know that Menchu's father did not **advocate** violence?

2. How might language have affected the ability of the native peoples of Guatemala to form a united opposition to the army?

3. What **reprisal** did government forces make for the occupation of the Spanish embassy?

4. What **atrocities** was Menchu's father subjected to?

5. What were the **dire** consequences for Menchu's family of the burning of the Spanish embassy?

6. What event will be **commemorated** in 2092?

7. Why would it be inaccurate to describe Rigoberta Menchu as **mute** about the suffering of the Guatemalan people?

8. Do you think that Menchu's family was part of the country's **elite**?

9. What is the meaning of **abject** as it is used in the passage?

10. Give one example from the passage of a **flagrant** abuse of human rights by the Guatemalan military.

11. How might the Guatemalan generals defend the army's treatment of protesters?

12. How do you know that the lives of the Guatemalans who fled to Mexico did not improve much?

13. How do you think Rigoberta Menchu's autobiography **enhanced** people's knowledge of what was happening in Guatemala?

14. What is the meaning of **wreaked** as it is used in the passage?

15. During the war, why were many Guatemalan peasants left homeless?

FUN & FASCINATING FACTS

The Latin prefix *ab-*, "from" or "away," combines with the root from the Latin verb *jacere*, "to throw," to form the adjective **abject**. When John Milton in *Paradise Lost* refers to the fallen angels in hell as "*abject* and lost," he was using the word in its original meaning, "cast out" or "rejected." It now means "wretched" or "in a low state."

The Latin *flagrare* means "to burn" and forms the root of the adjective **flagrant**. The original meaning of this word was "flaming" or "blazing," which changed over time to "outrageous" or "conspicuously bad." A blazing fire is certainly conspicuous, and perhaps it is this connection that led to the change in meaning.

One of the meanings of *raise* is "to build." It is curious then that **raze**, a word with the same pronunciation, has just the opposite meaning, "to destroy completely." (While it can take a team of workers several days to *raise* a barn, a tornado can *raze* it in a matter of minutes.)

Lesson 11

Word List
Study the definitions of the words below; then do the exercises for the lesson.

augment
ôg ment´

v. To increase in size, amount, or degree.
In order to buy a new bike before summer, Iris **augmented** her savings by baby-sitting the twins next door.

benign
bi nīn´

adj. 1. Kind; gracious; gentle.
Friendly nurses were a **benign** presence in the hospital.
2. Favorable; not threatening.
Although the weather had been **benign** when Harry and Laura had sailed out onto the lake in the morning, by noon, conditions had changed dramatically.

connoisseur
kän ə sʉr´

n. A person with extensive knowledge, especially of the fine arts; a person of refined taste.
A **connoisseur** of rare stamps would recognize the famous English "penny black" at once.

discern
di sʉrn´

v. 1. To detect with the eyes.
About forty-five minutes after the ferry left Block Island, the passengers could **discern** the coast of Rhode Island before them.
2. To understand or comprehend.
Not until she finished the novel did Janice **discern** the significance of the title.
3. To recognize as separate or different.
We made certain we could easily **discern** our luggage by putting red tape on the handle.
discerning *adj.* Having good judgment; perceptive.
Virginia's **discerning** comments about Jay's serve helped him to improve his tennis game.

embellish
em bel´ ish

v. 1. To make beautiful by adding decorative elements.
The entire surface of the black cloth had been **embellished** with colored threads stitched in elaborate patterns.
2. To add fictitious details to.
Mark Twain often **embellished** his stories to make them more interesting.

execute
ek´ sə kyo͞ot

v. 1. To carry out; to perform.
The driving instructor told me to **execute** a U-turn.
2. To create, as a work of art.
These paintings of William Merritt Chase were **executed** in oils during his summers at Shinnecock, Long Island.
3. To put to death as a legal penalty.
Executing criminals condemned to death is a controversial practice.

exemplify
ek zem´ pli fī

v. To illustrate by being an example of.
The poetry of Langston Hughes **exemplifies** some of the best work of the writers of the Harlem Renaissance.

grotesque
grō tesk´

adj. So distorted or strange as to appear bizarre or comical.
The **grotesque** masks worn by the dancers frightened the children.

hallowed hal´ ōd	*adj.* Greatly respected; holy; sacred. Arlington National Cemetery is **hallowed** ground because it is the burial place for soldiers who have died in war.
impersonate im pur´ sə nāt	*v.* 1. To assume the character or appearance of. The solution to the mystery became clear to the detective when he learned that one woman had **impersonated** another when renting the apartment. 2. To mimic. I tried to **impersonate** my mother when I answered the phone.
malevolent mə lev´ ə lənt	*adj.* Showing ill will or hatred; producing harm or evil. Iago's **malevolent** plan to encourage Othello's jealousy resulted in murder and suicide. **malevolence** *n.* A feeling or expression of ill will. The look of **malevolence** in his eyes sent shudders down our spines.
ornate ôr nāt´	*adj.* Heavily and elaborately decorated. The tour guide pointed out the **ornate** carving over the arched doorway.
pastoral pas´ tər əl	*adj.* 1. Having to do with shepherds and herders. The Industrial Revolution contributed to the disappearance of a **pastoral** way of life. 2. Relating to country life, and often presented as charmingly simple. Some of Corot's most appealing paintings are those that show **pastoral** scenes.
precarious prē kar´ ē əs	*adj.* Not safe or secure; dangerously uncertain. Having cut through the thick vines to get a better view of the waterfall, the hikers did not understand how **precarious** their situation was until they tried to return to the trail and could not find it.
renown rē noun´	*n.* Fame; honor. Sir Laurence Olivier, a British actor who died in 1989, achieved **renown** for his roles in Shakespeare's plays. **renowned** *adj.* Famous; honored. Samuel Johnson was a **renowned** literary figure in eighteenth-century England.

11A Finding Meanings

Choose two phrases to form a sentence that correctly uses a word from Word List 11. Write each sentence in the space provided.

1. (a) one that is friendly or kind.
   (b) A grotesque expression is
   (c) A benign expression is
   (d) one that is meant to deceive.

   _a c._

2. (a) add decoration to it.
   (b) To embellish something is to
   (c) take care of it.
   (d) To discern something is to

   _b a_

3. (a) one that is nonexistent.   (c) A hallowed location is
   (b) one that is insecure.   (d) A precarious location is

   db

4. (a) To exemplify something is to   (c) To impersonate something is to
   (b) be a good example of it.   (d) be frustrated by it.

   ab.

5. (a) To augment something   (c) To discern something
   (b) is to be unaware of it.   (d) is to notice it.

   c d.

6. (a) that has some practical use.   (c) A hallowed object is one
   (b) that is regarded as sacred.   (d) An ornate object is one

   c b.

7. (a) Renown is   (c) a show of understanding.
   (b) Malevolence is   (d) a feeling of intense ill will.

   bd.

8. (a) that is made of precious metal. (c) that is heavily decorated.
   (b) An ornate object is one   (d) A grotesque object is one

   b.c.

9. (a) To impersonate someone   (c) is to show admiration for that person.
   (b) is to put that person to death. (d) To execute someone

   db.

10. (a) is one that is famous.   (c) A pastoral novel
    (b) A renowned novel   (d) is one whose author is unknown.

    b.a

augment
benign
connoisseur
discern
embellish
execute
exemplify
grotesque
hallowed
impersonate
malevolent
ornate
pastoral
precarious
renown

11B Just the Right Word

Improve each of the following sentences by crossing out the bold phrase and replacing it with a word (or a form of the word) from Word List 11.

1. Luciano Pavarotti's **world-wide reputation** makes him easily recognizable.
   renowed

2. Mirta **increased the size of** her wardrobe by making several dresses during summer vacation. *augmented*

3. At the costume shop, we found just the mask we wanted—one with **horribly distorted** *grotesque*
features and green hair.

4. Even critics who were **able to perceive small differences** could not tell that the
painting was a fake. *discerned*

5. It is a crime to **dress up as and pretend to be** a police officer.
impersonate

6. Peggy Guggenheim was well known as a **person who was both knowledgeable about
and had a love** of modern art. *connoisseur*

exemplifies

7. The arch **is a good example of what is distinctive about** Roman architecture.

ornated

8. Simone **added a few extra details to** her account of the dog's rescue, suggesting that her
own role had been crucial.

9. Even though Alberto Giacometti **gave final form to** hundreds of sculptures, he never felt
they fully expressed what he meant. *executed*

10. In **The Winter's Tale**, Shakespeare alternates scenes in a **simple and unaffected
country** setting with those in the splendid palace of the king. *precarious*

11C Applying Meanings

Circle the letter of each correct answer to the questions below.
Questions may have more than one correct answer.

a.bc

1. Which of the following might be present in a **pastoral** scene?
   - (a) a shepherd
   - (b) a meadow
   - (c) a stream
   - (d) a skyscraper

ab

2. Which of the following can be **ornate**?
   - (a) a design
   - (b) a brooch
   - (c) an ordeal
   - (d) an inkling

3. Which of the following can be **discerned**?
   - (a) a slight fault
   - (b) a slight movement
   - (c) a slight difference
   - (d) an opportunity

4. Which of the following can be **executed**?
   - (a) a portrait
   - (b) a person
   - (c) a dance step
   - (d) an order

5. Which of the following can be **malevolent**?

   (a) an odor   ✓ (c) a grin

   (b) a pseudonym   ✓ (d) a person

6. Which of the following can be **impersonated**?

   (a) a friend's grades   ✓ (c) a friend's voice

  ✓ (b) a friend's brother   ✓ (d) a friend's walk

7. Which of the following can be **hallowed**?

   (a) a person's name   ✓ (c) a battlefield

  ✓ (b) a place of worship   ✓ (d) a person's memory

8. Which of the following can be **benign**?

   (a) an expression   ✓ (c) a growth on the skin

   (b) a tirade   ✓ (d) a climate

11D Word Study

Each group of four words below contains two words that are either synonyms or antonyms. Circle these two words, then circle the *S* if they are synonyms, the *A* if they are antonyms.

1. secure	benign	precarious	agile	S	A
2. turmoil	banter	audacity	tumult	S	A
3. intricate	unseemly	appropriate	mild	S	A
4. humdrum	inane	electrifying	offensive	S	A
5. kind	ornate	benevolent	bizarre	S	A
6. languish	simplify	impersonate	embellish	S	A
7. avid	agile	intricate	ornate	S	A
8. foolish	balmy	turbulent	gruesome	S	A
9. atrocious	fitful	commendable	crucial	S	A
10. slovenly	audible	fastidious	copious	S	A

augment

benign

connoisseur

discern

embellish

execute

exemplify

grotesque

hallowed

impersonate

malevolent

ornate

pastoral

precarious

renown

11E Passage

Read the passage below; then complete the exercise that follows.

The Kachina Dolls of Oraibi

The village of Oraibi lies in the middle of the four-thousand-square-mile Hopi Reservation in the northeast corner of Arizona. Believed to be the oldest continuously inhabited village in North America, it was first settled nearly a thousand years ago by the Anasazi, a **pastoral** people, who excelled in the creation of beautiful objects.

The descendants of the Anasazi, the Hopi people, now inhabit the area and continue the thousand-year-old tradition of making fine pottery, woven rugs, and baskets. But Hopi artistry is best **exemplified** by the unique form of carved wooden figures known as kachinas. These figures are sculpted from the root of the cottonwood tree and range in size from a few inches up to two feet. The heads often have **ornately** carved masks, while the finished figures are painted in bright colors and **embellished** with shells, feathers, and semiprecious stones.

The kachina carvings are representations of the Hopi spirit world. In the Hopi view, everything in the world is inhabited by a spirit; when people succeed in living in harmony and balance with the spirits, the world will be at peace. The carvings represent the spirits of **hallowed** figures from Hopi history as well as of plants and animals, the sun, the moon, and the stars.

From late December to late July, when the spirits are believed to be on Earth, the Hopi perform ceremonies in their villages. Masked and costumed dancers **impersonate** the spirits in celebrations held in their honor. Some of the dancers represent **benign**, gift-bearing kachinas who present children with carved dolls. These are not toys, for they have a religious and social significance, but neither are they worshiped as idols. They are hung on the walls of Hopi homes, and by learning what each kachina doll stands for, the children **discern** the history, codes of behavior, and religion of their people. Along with the gift-bearing kachinas, there are also representations of **malevolent** ones who dance through the village streets, supposedly searching for those in the community who have been disobedient. These demon kachinas are often **grotesque** in appearance, frightening to those who see them approaching.

Until the late nineteenth century, outside visitors were rare in Hopi villages; their inhabitants did not encourage such visits and the paths leading to the high, flat hilltops were very **precarious**. But once roads were built, access to the heights was easy; so the residents often were outnumbered by tourists who came to watch the religious ceremonies held in the spring and summer and to purchase kachina dolls as mementos. Hopi carvers, who once had made these dolls only for use in their own communities, stepped up production to meet the demand.

Gradually, the kachinas began to change. Tourists wanted larger carvings and figures showing action. The size of a kachina was **augmented** by the addition of other carved pieces attached by glue; and because many Hopi were opposed to the sale of their religious objects to outsiders, the figures were **executed** so that they differed from those used in Hopi ceremonies.

Today, many Hopi carvers continue the ancient tradition, using the same simple materials and tools of earlier generations. Collectors of Native American art purchase kachina dolls directly from these carvers or from gift shops that feature their work. Some carvers have achieved world **renown**, and their work commands prices in the thousands of dollars.

Connoisseurs of Hopi carving who travel to Oklahoma City will find over sixty Kachina dolls on permanent display at the National Cowboy Hall of Fame. In Phoenix, Arizona, the place to visit is the Heard Museum. It is famous for its collection of over four hundred dolls, many of them presented to the museum by Arizona's then Senator Barry Goldwater.

Answer each of the following questions in the form of a sentence. If a question does not contain a vocabulary word from this lesson's word list, use one in your answer. Use each word only once. Questions and answers will then contain all fifteen words (or forms of the words).

1. How do you know that Hopi dancers are not considered to be actual kachina spirits?

2. What is the purpose of the **malevolent** kachina dancers?

3. Before the end of the last century, why didn't many tourists visit the Hopi?

4. What detail tells you that the carvers spend a lot of time working on the heads of the dolls?

5. Why would it be inaccurate to say that the kachina dolls are very simple in style?

6. What is the meaning of **benign** as it is used in the passage?

7. How can people tell the difference between the demon kachina dancers and the gift-bearing kachina dancers?

8. Why did some Hopi oppose selling kachinas to outsiders?

9. How do you know that the ancestors of the Hopi raised sheep or goats?

10. What do the kachina carvings **exemplify**?

11. What is the meaning of **executed** as it is used in the passage?

12. What important role do kachina dolls play in the education of Hopi children?

13. Why is it likely that Barry Goldwater could have told you a lot about kachina carvings?

14. What change was made in the kachinas carved for outsiders?

15. Why do people visit the Hopi?

FUN & FASCINATING FACTS

The adjective **benign** is formed from the Latin *bene*, which means "well" or "good." The antonym of this word is *malignant*, formed from the Latin *mal*, which means "bad" or "evil."

A person seeing a doctor about a growth or tumor would be relieved to learn that it was *benign*; this would mean that it was harmless. The person would be very concerned if told the growth was *malignant*, for that would mean it was cancerous.

Malevolent is another word formed from the Latin *mal*. It is similar in meaning to *malicious*, but *malevolent* is a much stronger term. A *malicious* remark may hurt the person it is directed at, but could be simply mischievous; whereas, a *malevolent* remark suggests strong hatred on the part of the person making it.

Pastor is another name for minister in many churches; the English word comes from the Latin *pastor*, "a shepherd." The minister or pastor is looked upon by the congregation as a shepherd to his or her flock. The adjective formed from *pastor* is **pastoral**, which means "of or relating to country life, especially as it relates to the lives of shepherds and shepherdesses." Pastoral scenes have long been a favorite of painters because the subject suggests a peaceful and simple way of life. A *pastoral* is a poem or other literary or artistic work dealing with the quiet life of the country.

Lesson 12

Word List
Study the definitions of the words below; then do the exercises for the lesson.

accede
ak sēd´

v. To agree to; to consent to, often after urging from another.
Myron **acceded** to the wishes of his colleagues when he stopped smoking in the office.

affluent
af´ lōō ənt

adj. Generously supplied with money or possessions; wealthy.
Although Cicely was not from an **affluent** family, she could attend an excellent but expensive school because of the scholarship she had won.
affluence *n.* Wealth.
Mrs. Winn's **affluence** is due to oil being discovered on her land.

arbitrary
är´ bi trer ē

adj. Determined by chance or whim rather than by reason or necessity.
Even though our choice of restaurant was **arbitrary**, the food was delicious.

artisan
ärt´ ə zən

n. One able to do skilled work with the hands; a craftsperson.
Artisans working with leather, yarn, and clay displayed their products at the local crafts fair.

dismantle
dis mant´ l

v. To take apart.
Bert helped Matt **dismantle** the engine so they could begin work on the repair.

immerse
im mʉrs´

v. 1. To cover with liquid.
To prepare the salad, Genevieve first blanched the vegetables by **immersing** them in boiling water.
2. To completely engage the attention of.
Sophie, **immersed** in her book, did not notice when Jaime boarded the bus and sat down beside her.

irksome
ʉrk´ səm

adj. Annoying; tedious.
All the steps preliminary to painting the ceiling—scraping, patching, and sanding—were **irksome** to Samantha, who wanted to finish the job quickly.

legacy
leg´ ə sē

n. 1. Money or property left to another in a will.
This silver pocket watch is my **legacy** from Grandfather Gomez.
2. Something passed on to those who come after.
Catholicism and the Spanish language are **legacies** of Spanish rule in Guatemala.

ostentatious
äs tən tā´ shəs

adj. Extravagantly showy or ornate.
The Amish shun **ostentatious** furnishings for their homes.

panorama
pan ə ram´ ə

n. 1. A complete view of a surrounding area.
In one bedroom of the old mansion, the four walls had been painted with a lively **panorama** of Chesapeake Bay.
2. A thorough presentation of a subject.
One course my aunt teaches at the university is a **panorama** of civil rights law in the United States.

philanthropy	n. The attempt to improve the well-being of those in need by donating money or aid.
fi lan´ thrə pē	The **philanthropy** of the Tan family has provided the money for this cancer research center.
	philanthropist n. One who makes substantial contributions to those in need.
	Andrew Carnegie, a renowned **philanthropist**, established many public libraries in the early 1900s.

prestige	n. High standing; respect earned by accomplishments.
pres tēzh´	Winning the Nobel Prize brings much **prestige**.
	prestigious adj. (pres tij´ əs) Honored; esteemed.
	An Oscar is the most **prestigious** award in the movie industry.

| **prolific** | adj. Abundantly productive. |
| prō lif´ ik | Although Robert Graves was a **prolific** poet, he is remembered primarily for his few novels. |

reticent	adj. Inclined to keep one's thoughts and feelings to oneself; quiet and reserved.
ret´ ə sənt	When we asked her about her parents, Adriana grew **reticent**.
	reticence n. Silence or reserve.
	Karl's **reticence** about his plans for the summer made us even more curious.

| **tycoon** | n. A wealthy and powerful businessperson. |
| tī kōōn´ | Blithewold, once the summer residence of a coal-mining **tycoon**, now is open to tourists. |

12A Finding Meanings

Choose two phrases to form a sentence that correctly uses a word from Word List 12. Write each sentence in the space provided.

1. (a) A panorama is
   (b) An artisan is
   (c) a powerful businessperson.
   (d) a complete view in all directions.

2. (a) An ostentatious poet is one who
   (b) produces a large body of work.
   (c) is greatly honored and respected.
   (d) A prolific poet is one who

3. (a) A reticent person
   (b) is conscientious and reliable.
   (c) An affluent person
   (d) is quiet and says little.

4. (a) a person with refined taste.
   (b) A tycoon is
   (c) An artisan is
   (d) a worker skilled at a trade or craft.

5. (a) put it back together.
   (b) To immerse something is to
   (c) To dismantle something is to
   (d) cover it with liquid.

6. (a) Philanthropy is   (c) a willingness to take risks.
   (b) Affluence is   (d) making contributions to those in need.

7. (a) a wind of hurricane force.   (c) A legacy is
   (b) a sum of money left to a person. (d) A tycoon is

8. (a) An irksome position   (c) is one that is annoying.
   (b) A prestigious position   (d) is one that pays a great deal.

9. (a) An ostentatious review   (c) is one designed to draw much attention.
   (b) An arbitrary review   (d) is one that can be shown to be in error.

10. (a) To accede to something   (c) To dismantle something
    (b) is to agree to it.   (d) is to find fault with it.

12B Just the Right Word

Improve each of the following sentences by crossing out the bold phrase and replacing it with a word (or a form of the word) from Word List 12.

accede

affluent

arbitrary

artisan

dismantle

immerse

irksome

legacy

ostentatious

panorama

philanthropy

prestige

prolific

reticent

tycoon

1. The objects excavated from the ruins of Pompeii suggest that many people who lived there had been **in possession of great wealth**.

2. Dora recommends this book because it provides a **complete and unbroken view** of Polish history.

3. Blanca's **tendency to keep her thoughts to herself** makes it difficult to get to know her.

4. My bicycle is easy to **break down into its separate parts** if I want to take it on the plane.

5. Giselle was **completely absorbed** in her science project when the phone rang.

6. Umpire Heller denied that his call was **based on personal whim**.

7. Mount Helos Hospital is the most **respected because of its high standing** in the state.

8. In the 1940s the Lee family, local **people who gave to those in need**, built this concert hall, which still serves the community.

9. This book suggests that one **of the things handed down as a result** of the 1960s was a greater awareness of equal rights for all Americans.

10. A **rich and powerful businessperson** from Brazil is interested in buying this jewelry factory.

12C Applying Meanings

Circle the letter of each correct answer to the questions below. Questions may have more than one correct answer.

1. Which of the following might describe the actions of a **philanthropist**?
   (a) benign
   (b) prudent
   (c) despicable
   (d) spontaneous

2. Which of the following might be a **legacy**?
   (a) a coin collection
   (b) a democratic government
   (c) a savings bond
   (d) a tirade

3. Which of the following might earn you **prestige**?
   (a) buying a new bicycle
   (b) winning a scholarship
   (c) doing your chores
   (d) beating a track record

4. Which of the following can be **dismantled**?
   (a) a sewing machine
   (b) a light bulb
   (c) a book
   (d) a loaf of bread

5. In which of the following could one be **immersed**?
   (a) laughter
   (b) a conversation
   (c) a movie
   (d) water

6. Which of the following is an **artisan**?
   (a) a stonemason
   (b) a bus driver
   (c) a basket weaver
   (d) a firefighter

7. Which of the following might be considered a **tycoon**?
   (a) an oil billionaire
   (b) a college president
   (c) a state governor
   (d) the head of a computer company

8. Which of the following suggests **affluence**?
   (a) owning expensive jewelry
   (b) living in an apartment
   (c) flying on one's own jet
   (d) buying a pair of shoes

12D Word Study

Complete the analogies by selecting the pair of words whose relationship most resembles the relationship of the pair in capital letters. Circle the letter in front of the pair you choose.

1. AFFLUENCE : POVERTY ::
   - (a) money : wealth
   - (b) stupidity : inanity
   - (c) agility : speed
   - (d) joy : despair

2. ASSEMBLE : DISMANTLE ::
   - (a) augment : increase
   - (b) entangle : extricate
   - (c) pilfer : steal
   - (d) interrogate : question

3. STRANGE : GROTESQUE ::
   - (a) sporadic : constant
   - (b) naughty : malevolent
   - (c) blue : azure
   - (d) prudent : careful

4. CONNOISSEUR : TASTE ::
   - (a) sage : wisdom
   - (b) fledgling : flight
   - (c) proprietor : property
   - (d) colleague : business

5. ACROBAT : AGILITY ::
   - (a) judge : jury
   - (b) philanthropist : gift
   - (c) doctor : health
   - (d) tycoon : wealth

6. BENIGN : MALEVOLENT ::
   - (a) ornate : intricate
   - (b) good : evil
   - (c) unseemly : flagrant
   - (d) cool : warm

7. RAZE : RAISE ::
   - (a) discern : see
   - (b) accede : agree
   - (c) exemplify : illustrate
   - (d) destroy : build

8. TURMOIL : ORDER ::
   - (a) legacy : property
   - (b) dialect : language
   - (c) anarchy : law
   - (d) staple : sugar

9. AUGMENT : INCREASE ::
   - (a) enhance : improve
   - (b) admit : deny
   - (c) precede : follow
   - (d) lend : borrow

10. PRESTIGE : PRESTIGIOUS ::
    - (a) tumult : tumultuous
    - (b) panorama : unseemly
    - (c) danger : precarious
    - (d) banter : humorous

accede
affluent
arbitrary
artisan
dismantle
immerse
irksome
legacy
ostentatious
panorama
philanthropy
prestige
prolific
reticent
tycoon

Read the passage below; then complete the exercise that follows.

Hearst Castle's Master Builder

As part of their tour, visitors to Hearst Castle, also known as San Simeon, in southern California, are shown home movies of the many celebrities who were guests there during the 1930s and 1940s. In one film, a tiny, bespectacled woman hiding her face behind a sheaf of papers is mistakenly identified by the narrator as William Randolph Hearst's secretary. In fact, she was Julia Morgan, the architect who designed and supervised the building of the castle, which some have described as the most **ostentatious** residence of the twentieth century.

There is an explanation for the error. Julia Morgan, despite being an extremely **prolific** architect, with over seven hundred buildings to her credit, was a very **reticent** person who actively avoided publicity for herself. From early in her career, she rarely gave interviews. When she retired at the age of 79, she had all her architectural drawings destroyed, declaring that the buildings themselves would be her **legacy**. As a result, very little was written about her for many years.

Julia Morgan was born into an **affluent** San Francisco family in 1872. Although it was not common for young women to attend college, she entered the engineering school at the University of California at Berkeley. After graduation, she became the first woman admitted as an architectural student to the **prestigious** École des Beaux Arts in Paris, France. When her studies were completed, she returned to California, ready to open her own firm. First, however, she had to pass the state licensing exam, which she did in 1904, becoming the first woman to receive an architectural license to practice in that state.

Morgan had great skill in understanding her clients' wishes and in carrying them out successfully as she designed and built private homes as well as public buildings. One of her clients was Mrs. Phoebe Hearst, a wealthy widow and **philanthropist**. When Mrs. Hearst died in 1919, her only child, the publishing **tycoon** William Randolph Hearst, inherited her enormous fortune. To match his great wealth, he had extravagant plans—a home to be built on his 275,000-acre ranch, midway between San Francisco and Los Angeles. For this project, he hired Julia Morgan.

For the next twenty years, Morgan **immersed** herself in every aspect of the design and construction of the main house and three guest houses. Early in the project she supervised the laying of five miles of road to provide access to the site and arranged for a dock to be built to receive building materials arriving by ship. As the buildings were completed, she brought skilled **artisans** from Europe to execute the wood and stone carvings that embellish many of the rooms.

From the beginning, Hearst was actively involved in the building of "the ranch," as he called it. At times, this must have been **irksome**; for example, when an elaborate fireplace that had been completed had to be **dismantled** and moved to a different place in the same room because Hearst was dissatisfied with its location. Morgan had no choice but to **accede** to Hearst's wishes when he **arbitrarily** changed his mind, as he frequently did.

The scope of the project provided Morgan with a unique challenge as an architect. Casa Grande, the main house, contains 115 rooms, filled with art treasures collected in Europe. Its twin towers, 137 feet high, offer a fine **panorama** of the Pacific Ocean and the Santa Lucia mountains. The outdoor Neptune pool, lined with green and white marble, is not only breathtakingly beautiful but also soundly constructed on its hillside site. In addition to the buildings, Morgan directed the creation of numerous gardens and a private zoo that grew to include more than 100 species.

By the late 1930s, construction at San Simeon ceased. Morgan continued to work on other projects for Hearst as well as for other clients, until 1951, when she retired. In 1958, San Simeon became one of

California's state historical monuments. With over one million visitors a year, it is now one of the nation's most popular tourist attractions. Everyone knows that it was Hearst's millions that paid for it, but very few know the name of the person who designed and supervised its building. And that is the way Julia Morgan would have wanted it.

Answer each of the following questions in the form of a sentence. If a question does not contain a vocabulary word from this lesson's word list, use one in your answer. Use each word only once. Questions and answers will then contain all fifteen words (or forms of the words).

1. Give some details of the San Simeon project that show that William Randolph Hearst was an **affluent** man.

2. What has been the result of Julia Morgan's **reticence**?

3. Why do you think Morgan brought **artisans** from Europe to do the carvings?

4. How do you know that Hearst was successful with his business?

5. How do you know that Morgan did not find Hearst too **irksome** to work with?

6. Why might fireplaces have to be **dismantled** before being moved?

7. What details in the passage suggest that Hearst's taste was rather **ostentatious**?

8. Was Hearst Castle Morgan's only project? Explain.

9. Why would Morgan have to **accede** to Hearst's decisions about the Castle?

10. Why must Hearst's frequent changes have been hard to accept?

11. Why do you think Morgan included towers as part of the design of the main house?

12. What is the meaning of **immersed** as it is used in the passage?

13. Why would it be inaccurate to describe San Simeon as a **philanthropic** project?

14. What is the meaning of **legacy** as it is used in the passage?

15. What details in the passage suggest that Morgan deserves a position of **prestige** among American architects?

FUN & FASCINATING FACTS

Commodore Matthew C. Perry's visit to Japan in 1854 opened that country for the first time to trade with the United States. It also added a new word to the English language. Perry negotiated with a Japanese official whose title was *taikun*. This was formed from two Chinese words, *ta,* "great," and *kiun*, "prince." Perry introduced the word on his return to the United States, and it caught on. The spelling became modified to **tycoon**. During Abraham Lincoln's presidency, members of his cabinet affectionately referred to him by that term, *tycoon*.

Another English word of Chinese origin is *typhoon*, a wind of hurricane force in the western Pacific, formed from *ta,* "great," and *feng,* "wind."

The Greek verb *philein*, "to love," combines with the Greek *anthropos,* "humankind," to form **philanthropist**. Other words formed from *philein* include: *bibliophile*, "a person who loves and collects books"; *Anglophile*, "a person who loves England and the English"; *Francophile*, "a person who loves France and the French"; *philosophy*, "the love of and seeking after wisdom"; and *philology*, "the love of words and language."

Review for Lessons 9–12

Crossword Puzzle Solve the crossword puzzle below by studying the clues and filling in the answer boxes. Clues followed by a number are definitions of words in Lessons 9 through 12. The number gives the word list in which the answer to the clue appears.

Clues Across

1. Uproar or disturbance (9)
4. Abundantly productive (12)
7. We breathe it
9. Extravagantly showy (12)
10. To detect with the eyes (11)
12. Quickness of mind or body (9)
14. A food such as sugar or flour (9)
15. Two times five
18. An oak, for example
20. A state of confusion (10)
22. It comes from a sheep
23. Happening irregularly (9)
24. To carry out or perform (11)
25. A pistachio, for example
26. Something kept as a reminder (9)

Clues Down

2. Unable or unwilling to speak (10)
3. To lose hope, strength, or vitality (10)
4. Private giving to those in need (12)
5. Annoying; tedious (12)
6. Soothing, mild (9)
7. To assist in a questionable activity (9)
8. Fame; honor (11)
9. Heavily decorated (9)
11. To distribute as a portion or share (9)
13. To cover with liquid (12)
15. A wealthy businessperson (12)
16. Favorable; not threatening (11)
17. Opposite of *clean*
19. Considered superior to others (10)
21. Opposite of *false*

Lesson 13

Word List   Study the definitions of the words below; then do the exercises for the lesson.

ardent
är´ dənt

adj. Intensely eager; passionate.
In spite of Miriam's **ardent** praise of Walter, I was not convinced of his ability.
ardor *n.* Passionate intensity of feeling.
Romeo's **ardor** led him to take great risks to see his beloved Juliet.

assail
ə sāl´

v. 1. To attack violently or verbally.
Critics **assailed** the book when it first appeared but the reading public loved it.
2. To trouble in the mind.
Feelings of remorse **assailed** Lord Jim for his single act of cowardice.

asset
a´ set

n. 1. Anything owned that is of value and can be sold or otherwise disposed of.
The late Mr. Kim's **assets** include a valuable stamp collection.
2. A quality that can be used to advantage.
Height can be a great **asset** in a basketball player.

barter
bär´ tər

v. To exchange goods or services without the use of money.
Money was of little use in Plymouth Colony so the Pilgrims **bartered** with the Native Americans for the things they needed.
n. The exchange of goods or services without the use of money.
Commerce was conducted by **barter** when Iraq's currency collapsed after the 2003 invasion.

bonanza
bə nan´ zə

n. A source of great wealth; something that brings great riches.
The musical "Cats" was a **bonanza** for the estate of T.S. Eliot, as he wrote the book of poems on which it is based.

contagious
kən tā´ jəs

adj. Able to be passed easily from one person to another.
They say that laughter is **contagious**.

contemplate
kän´ təm plāt

v. 1. To give careful thought to; to ponder.
Einstein **contemplated** the relationship between matter and energy.
2. To have plans to; to intend.
While still playing basketball, Michael Jordan **contemplated** becoming a professional baseball player.

deter
dē tʉr´

v. To discourage or prevent from taking action.
Yesterday's rough seas **deterred** the divers from exploring the sunken ship.
deterrent *n.* Anything that prevents or discourages.
A "Keep Off" sign acts as a **deterrent** against trespassers.

flair
flãr

n. A natural gift or ability; a talent.
Jimmy Doo's **flair** for bantering with audience members made him a popular entertainer.

forfeit
fôr´ fit

v. To be forced to give up or lose.
If you leave the stadium before the end of the concert, you **forfeit** the right to return.
n. Something lost or given up as a result of an error or failing.
You have to pay a **forfeit** if you can't answer the question.

innovation in ə vā´ shən	*n.* Something new; a new way of doing something. Adding sound to movies was an **innovation** that transformed the film industry. **innovative** (i´ nə vā tiv) *adj.* Marked by freshness or originality; willing to try new things. Companies succeed by being **innovative** and keeping up with the latest technology.
mania mā´ ne ə	*n.* An intense or extreme enthusiasm or excitement. The trendy new video game system caused a **mania** in toy stores.
stymie stī´ mē	*v.* To thwart; to make difficulties for or find problems with. Attempts to make super-conductive materials were **stymied** by the extremely low temperatures required.
synonymous si non´ ə məs	*adj.* Alike or close in meaning; closely related. The company boasts that its name is **synonymous** with quality.
wrangle raŋ´ gəl	*v.* To quarrel in a noisy or angry way. Sue and Mario **wrangled** over whose turn it was to cut the grass.

13A Finding Meanings

Choose two phrases to form a sentence that correctly uses a word from Word List 13. Write each sentence in the space provided.

1. (a) is to recover it.
   (b) is to consider it.
   (c) To contemplate something
   (d) To barter something

2. (a) a new method or improvement.
   (b) An innovation is
   (c) A mania is
   (d) a collection of objects.

3. (a) To be stymied
   (b) To be contagious
   (c) is to be friendly.
   (d) is to be thwarted.

4. (a) anything that discourages or prevents.
   (b) A deterrent is
   (c) A flair is
   (d) a bright signal light.

5. (a) Ardor is
   (b) Barter is
   (c) intensity of feeling.
   (d) an act of spite or revenge.

6. (a) is to receive it.
   (b) To assail something
   (c) is to attack it.
   (d) To forfeit something

ardent
assail
asset
barter
bonanza
contagious
contemplate
deter
flair
forfeit
innovation
mania
stymie
synonymous
wrangle

7. (a) A bonanza is   (c) an irrational fear.
   (b) A flair is   (d) a source of riches.

8. (a) is to use it up or exhaust it.   (c) is to have to give it up.
   (b) To forfeit something   (d) To barter something

9. (a) To be contagious is to be   (c) of unknown authorship.
   (b) To be synonymous is to be   (d) passed easily to others.

10. (a) To barter is to   (c) To wrangle is to
    (b) quarrel or argue.   (d) to help or encourage.

13B Just the Right Word

Improve each of the following sentences by crossing out the bold word or phrase and replacing it with a word (or a form of the word) from Word List 13.

1. To Sid's mom, motorcycles and danger are **closely related in her mind**.

2. Maisie is **making plans for** six months of travel in Bolivia before resuming her studies.

3. "I don't understand this **intense and uncontrollable desire** for shopping," said Grandpa crossly.

4. Don't let a minor setback **keep** you from doing what is best for you.

5. The twins began to **quarrel in a noisy manner** over whose turn it was.

6. The ability to identify with voters' concerns is a great **quality that can be used to advantage** when running for public office.

7. The society had no need of money as it survived economically by **exchanging goods and services with others**.

8. The poet has many admirers, and they are all **full of passionate intensity** in their support.

9. If the defendant does not show up, the money he paid to the court is **kept by those who were holding it**.

10. When it comes to making friends, Pam has a real **ability that seems to come naturally to her**.

13C Applying Meanings

Circle the letter of each correct answer to the questions below. Questions may have more than one correct answer.

1. Which of the following were at one time considered an **innovation**?
   (a) parents
   (b) waterfalls
   (c) computers
   (d) radio

2. Which of the following might be a **deterrent** to someone?
   (a) threats of punishment
   (b) hope of reward
   (c) offers of friendship
   (d) fear of failure

3. Which of the following might exhibit **ardor**?
   (a) an advocate
   (b) a painting
   (c) a fanatic
   (d) a connoisseur

4. Which of the following can **stymie** someone?
   (a) a problem
   (b) a mystery
   (c) a riddle
   (d) an equation

5. For which of the following might one have a **flair**?
   (a) languishing in prison
   (b) impersonating celebrities
   (c) taking out the trash
   (d) hot air ballooning

6. Which of the following could **assail** someone?
   (a) doubts
   (b) blows
   (c) fears
   (d) threats

7. Which of the following can be an **asset**?
   (a) money
   (b) good health
   (c) a gold watch
   (d) knowledge

8. Which of the following could be **bartered**?
   (a) food
   (b) labor
   (c) cash
   (d) a table

ardent

assail

asset

barter

bonanza

contagious

contemplate

deter

flair

forfeit

innovation

mania

stymie

synonymous

wrangle

13D Word Study

Choose from the two words provided and use each word only once when filling in the spaces. One space should be left blank.

assailed/attacked

1. The president was _____ from every quarter by bad news.

2. Everyone agrees that the dog _____ the mail carrier.

3. Jonah _____ the ball with a mighty swing and sent it out of the ballpark.

bartered/exchanged

4. I went to the store and _____ the sweater I'd bought for a larger size.

5. She says she _____ the house for over a million dollars.

6. The Pilgrims _____ manufactured goods for food brought by the Wampanoags.

deter/discourage

7. Temperatures of over 700 degrees _____ life from forming on Venus.

8. We _____ people who have no experience from applying for the job.

9. The high admission standards are designed to _____ all but the most gifted applicants.

discern/detect

10. After staring at the puzzle for a while, I began to _____ a pattern.

11. If there's carbon monoxide present, this gadget will _____ it immediately.

12. I _____ that Millie hardly ever goes out of the house these days.

enhance / improve

13. They decided to _____ the journey by going first-class.

14. A course in etiquette would _____ her manners.

15. A new kitchen will certainly _____ the value of your home.

13E Passage

Read the passage below; then complete the exercise that follows.

More Than Just a Pretty Flower

The Winkel family lived in the town of Alkmaar in Holland. There was Mr. Winkel himself, his wife Elisabeth, and their seven children. Winkel had a **flair** for business, and the family was well provided for. He kept a tavern in Alkmaar and also raised tulips, which were just then becoming fashionable in Holland. Sadly, sometime between 1631 and 1635 (the date is uncertain), Elisabeth died, leaving her husband a widower with three boys and four young girls to care for.

More misfortune was to follow; in 1636, Mr. Winkel died. In those days, it was not uncommon for children to lose both parents, and in fact, the Winkel children were luckier than most. Thanks to its trade with the East Indies, Holland was one of the wealthiest countries in Europe. Money was being poured into fine houses in Amsterdam and Haarlem, into paintings and other works of art (this was the age of Rembrandt and Franz Hals), and into all manner of luxury goods. But money also went into such **innovations** as government-run orphanages. And it was to the Alkmaar orphanage that the seven Winkel children were taken, where, you may be sure, they were very unhappy, although well cared for by the standards of the time.

Winkel's **assets** had been the tavern, worth very little, and his patch of tulip bulbs planted several years earlier. In the spring of 1636, just before he died, records show that he owned about seventy bulbs, prized for their rarity and beauty, as well as a number of lesser varieties. Several years earlier, the prices that some bulbs fetched at tulip auctions had begun to rise, slowly at first. The trend accelerated as more and more people saw a rare opportunity to get rich. Prices could double in a week. It was important to act quickly.

Soon, single bulbs were selling for hundreds, then thousands of guilders. This was at a time when a carpenter's annual earnings were about 250 guilders a year. For a deposit of a hundred guilders and a written promise to pay the balance at a later date, a person could buy a bulb worth a thousand guilders. Then it was just a matter of waiting for the price to double and sell the bulb for a profit of a thousand guilders. A carpenter could make as much in a week as he could by working for four years! Repeat this a few times and he could now **contemplate** a life of ease. To raise the hundred guilders, of course, he had to sell his tools.

Greed is **contagious**! The number of buyers increased rapidly even as the supply of bulbs remained unchanged. Those who had been indifferent to the tulip craze now became **ardent** bidders at the bulb auctions held throughout the land. Most knew little or nothing of business, or of tulips for that matter, but that did not **deter** buyers.

The **mania** was at its height by February 5, 1637, when Winkel's collection of tulip bulbs was sold at auction, the proceeds to be shared among his children, who, you may remember, were living at the Alkmaar orphanage. Those attending were, for the most part, wealthy connoisseurs seeking to add to their already exquisite collections. This was a unique opportunity for them to obtain some of the rarest, most beautiful tulips in the world, for Mr. Winkel had known just what he was doing when he planted his tulip patch several years earlier. That night, the bidding exceeded the most wildly optimistic forecasts. Seventy exceptionally rare tulip bulbs, plus a number of lesser varieties, realized ninety thousand guilders (about twelve million today in U.S. dollars).

Almost immediately, those involved in the tulip trade were **assailed** by doubts. Surely, prices couldn't possibly go any higher. All at once everyone wanted to sell and no one wanted to buy. Buyers and sellers were **stymied** in their efforts to settle accounts. Those who had previously agreed to buy refused to take delivery and **forfeited** their deposits. Those who had **bartered** their homes for a tulip bulb were now homeless.

The Winkel children were not involved in any of this **wrangling**. The three boys and four little girls were rich, and their **bonanza** was secure. But thousands of bewildered traders in the bulb business were ruined. Ironically, Holland never lost its love for tulips. In fact, Holland and tulips are **synonymous** to this day, as any visitor to that country will tell you.

Answer each of the following questions in the form of a sentence. If a question does not contain a vocabulary word from this lesson's word list, use one in your answer. Use each word only once. Questions and answers will then contain all fifteen words (or forms of the words).

1. Before 1630, what were the Winkel family's **assets**?

2. Trade meant wealth for Holland. Give some examples of what wealth brought.

3. Explain how the rise in price of bulbs gave a worker a future to **contemplate**.

4. Did Winkel have good business sense?

5. What does **contagious** mean as it is used in the passage?

6. What should have **deterred** bidders at the bulb auctions?

7. When did the **mania** for tulip sales reach its height?

8. What happened to the **ardor** of bidders after this date?

9. If bulb traders were **assailed** by doubts, how did that affect the business?

10. The word **stymie** originated in golf. It meant an object that obstructed a ball or another ball that obstructed a ball. What **stymied** bulb trade?

11. What did many **forfeit**?

12. How did some become homeless?

13. Before the trade collapsed, who enjoyed a **bonanza**?

14. What do you think the ruined traders were **wrangling** about?

15. If Holland is **synonymous** with tulips, what might Hawaii be **synonymous** with?

FUN & FASCINATING FACTS

Don't confuse **flair** with its homophone *flare*, "a bright light used as a signal."

As well as being a complete word by itself, **mania** attaches to a number of roots to form other words related to mental illness. These include: *pyromania*, an uncontrollable desire to start fires; *kleptomania*, an uncontrollable desire to steal; and *trichotillomania*, an uncontrollable desire to pull out one's own hair.

Wrangle has an additional meaning to that given in the glossary, one that comes from the days of the Old West. To cowboys, wrangling meant herding cattle. In fact, wrangler is another name for cowboy. If a dispute arose while doing their job, a pair of cowboys could wrangle cattle and wrangle with one another, even on horseback.

Lesson 14

> ## Word List
Study the definitions of the words below; then do the exercises for the lesson.

congenial
kən jēn´ yəl

adj. 1. Getting along well with others; affable.
The people in the small Italian town were very **congenial** when the tourist asked many questions.
2. Suited to one's needs or tastes; agreeable.
We found a **congenial** little cabin right on the beach.

decipher
dē sī´ fər

v. 1. To convert from a code or secret writing into ordinary language; to decode.
You **decipher** the code by replacing numbers with the corresponding letters.
2. To interpret the meaning of something puzzling; to solve.
The writing in these old letters is so faded that it is almost impossible to **decipher** the words.

dissect
di sekt´

v. 1. To cut into in order to study.
Students taking the biology course **dissect** a dead frog in order to learn about the internal organs.
2. To study closely; to analyze.
After Coach Willard and the team members had watched the video of last week's game, they **dissected** the plays that had gone wrong.

enigma
ə nig´ mə

n. Anything that is puzzling, mysterious, or hard to figure out.
Even after many studies, the purpose of the huge, complex designs formed in the dirt of the Peruvian desert remains an **enigma**.
enigmatic *adj.* (en ig mat´ ik) Puzzling; mysterious.
After I heard Lucia's **enigmatic** phone message, I called her immediately to find out what was going on.

ineffectual
in ə fek´ chōō əl

adj. Not bringing about the desired result, futile.
My attempt to grow tomato plants from seed has been **ineffectual**, with most withering before they had sprouted leaves.

infallible
in fal´ ə bəl

adj. 1. Incapable of making an error; never wrong.
Peterson's book is an **infallible** guide to the birds of the salt marshes.
2. Unlikely to fail or go wrong.
Rubbing a nettle sting with dock leaves is an **infallible** remedy.

irrepressible
ir rē pres´ ə bəl

adj. Incapable of being controlled or held back.
Charlie's **irrepressible** sense of humor helps to make history class fun.

luminous
lōō´ mə nəs

adj. 1. Giving off light.
Do you have a watch with a **luminous** face that you can bring on our camping trip?
2. Clear; easy to understand.
Jennie's history teacher praised her **luminous** prose in her research paper on the mill girls of Lowell.

millennium
mi len´ ē əm

n. A period of one thousand years.
A **millennium** is ten times as long as the one-hundred year period of a century.

mire
mīr

n. An area of wet, swampy ground; deep mud.
Last night's heavy rains have turned the field into a **mire**, delaying the planting of seed for several days.
v. To get stuck as if in a mire; unable to make progress.
The organizers of the road race became **mired** in a bewildering set of rules and regulations.

pestilence
pes´ tə ləns

n. A rapidly spreading and usually fatal disease.
The **pestilence** that swept through Europe in the 1300s killed three-quarters of the population.

stagnate
stag´ nāt

v. To fail to develop, change, or move.
Students' minds may **stagnate** if they are not challenged.
stagnant *adj.* (stag´ nənt) Not moving, changing, or developing.
As we approached the edge of the lake, we found **stagnant**, muddy water instead of the cold clear ripples we had expected.

sublime
sə blīm´

adj. Great or noble in expression, thought, or manner; splendid.
Standing on the rim of the Grand Canyon at dawn, we had a **sublime** panorama of the canyon walls changing color in the morning light.

vie
vī

v. To compete for, as in a contest.
By January, the top eight schools in the state **vied** for the championship.

voluminous
və loom´ ə nəs

adj. Having great bulk or volume; ample.
The museum will exhibit a select group of bowls and jugs from its **voluminous** collection of Pueblo pottery.

14A Finding Meanings

Choose two phrases to form a sentence that correctly uses a word from Word List 14. Write each sentence in the space provided.

congenial
decipher
dissect
enigma
ineffectual
infallible
irrepressible
luminous
millennium
mire
pestilence
stagnate
sublime
vie
voluminous

1. (a) is to prefer one's own company.　(c) To be congenial
   (b) is to be unable to control one's self.　(d) To be irrepressible

2. (a) a swamp.　(c) A mire is
   (b) a serious disagreement.　(d) A pestilence is

3. (a) A sublime poem　(c) is one that is unintentionally humorous.
   (b) An enigmatic poem　(d) is one that uplifts and ennobles.

4. (a) give up too easily.　(c) fail to change or develop.
   (b) To stagnate is to　(d) To vie is to

5. (a) A congenial person is one
   (b) who gets along easily with others.
   (c) An enigmatic person is one
   (d) who works tirelessly.

6. (a) To decipher something
   (b) To dissect something
   (c) is to make out what it says.
   (d) is to put it back together.

7. (a) one that is extremely lengthy.
   (b) one that has illustrations.
   (c) A voluminous account is
   (d) A luminous account is

8. (a) A millennium is
   (b) a fatal, rapidly spreading disease.
   (c) A pestilence is
   (d) a mass movement of people.

9. (a) one that is difficult to understand.
   (b) one that always works.
   (c) An infallible remedy is
   (d) An ineffectual remedy is

10. (a) to cut into it in order to study it.
    (b) to obtain it by underhanded means.
    (c) To vie for something is
    (d) To dissect something is

14B Just the Right Word

Improve each of the following sentences by crossing out the bold phrase and replacing it with a word (or a form of the word) from Word List 14.

1. Even though we boarded up the windows before the hurricane to protect them, our efforts were **not successful**.

2. The four students on our science team will **answer questions to compete** with other student teams from all over the country.

3. What role Ms. Layton had in the store fire remains an **unclear puzzle that no one has been able to figure out** to this day.

4. Claribel's enthusiasm for skydiving was **too strong for her to keep quiet about.**

5. The **rapidly spreading and usually fatal disease** affected rich and poor alike.

6. When Aunt Anne developed asthma, she moved to Arizona where she found the dry climate very **suitable to her medical requirements.**

7. The year 2001 marked the beginning of the third **period of one thousand years.**

8. Grandmother's eyes were **bright and seemed to glow with light** as she talked of her son, my father.

9. George felt **unable to proceed in any way while he was involved** in credit-card debt.

10. The notes to this edition of Shakespeare's plays are **extensive and take up many pages.**

14C Applying Meanings

Circle the letter of each correct answer to the questions below. Questions may have more than one correct answer.

1. Which of the following can be **luminous?**
   - (a) the moon
   - (b) a poem
   - (c) a painting
   - (d) a calamity

2. Which of the following can be **infallible?**
   - (a) a guide
   - (b) an injury
   - (c) a rock
   - (d) a remedy

3. Which of the following could be **stagnant?**
   - (a) water
   - (b) air
   - (c) an organization
   - (d) a society

congenial
decipher
dissect
enigma
ineffectual
infallible
irrepressible
luminous
millennium
mire
pestilence
stagnate
sublime
vie
voluminous

4. Which of the following can be **deciphered?**
   - (a) a message
   - (b) a word
   - (c) a tool
   - (d) a quarrel

5. For which of the following might people **vie?**
   - (a) a prize
   - (b) an advantage
   - (c) a reward
   - (d) a job

6. Which of the following can be **sublime?**
   - (a) a poem
   - (b) a laugh
   - (c) a painting
   - (d) a crime

7. Which of the following can be **dissected**?

(a) a body   (c) a report

(b) a problem   (d) a kidney

8. Which of the following can be **irrepressible**?

(a) joy   (c) laughter

(b) a recluse   (d) a flood

14D Word Study

Change each of the nouns below into an adjective by changing, adding, or dropping the suffix. Write the word in the space provided. Both forms of all of the words in this exercise are from this or an earlier lesson.

1. malevolence   _____

2. innovation   _____

3. prestige   _____

4. agility   _____

5. affluence   _____

6. atrocity   _____

7. inanity   _____

8. tumult   _____

9. ardor   _____

10. renown   _____

11. reticence   _____

12. enigma   _____

Read the passage below; then complete the exercise that follows.

Leonardo da Vinci: Renaissance Man

The word *renaissance* means "rebirth" and is applied to the reawakening of interest in learning and the arts that began in Italy in the fifteenth century. This brought to an end the **millennium** known as the Middle Ages, during which learning and the arts **stagnated**. It is impossible to set precise dates for the Renaissance, but it began to flower around 1450, and Leonardo da Vinci (1452–1517) is considered by many to be its supreme genius.

Leonardo was born in the small village of Vinci, near Florence, and as a youth studied painting and drawing in the workshop of the distinguished teacher Andrea del Verrocchio. His **congenial** disposition soon made him a popular member of Florence's artistic circles, while his extraordinary artistic ability, coupled with an **irrepressible** curiosity about the workings of nature, gave promise of his future greatness. His mind teemed with fresh ideas about music, science, and mathematics, a condition that exemplified the new spirit of the age. Leonardo would learn, not from the ancient writings of classical Greece and Rome, long regarded as **infallible** guides to everything from the movements of the heavens to the workings of the human body, but from the world he saw about him.

In his thirtieth year, Leonardo moved to Milan to serve as a military engineer at the court of Ludovico Sforza. Shortly after his arrival, the city was devastated by the **pestilence** known variously as the Plague or the Black Death. The traditional view was that such events were sent by God to punish the wicked. In contrast, Leonardo's idea was to clean up the slums in hopes of preventing this tragedy from happening again. He filled his **voluminous** notebooks with designs for many projects, including the layout of towns, the building of churches, and improvements in weapons of war. He even drew up plans for submarines and helicopters. He wrote his notes in a left-handed "mirror script" that can only be **deciphered** by holding them to a mirror and reading their reflection.

Leonardo lived during a turbulent period when political power rested with individual city-states that **vied** with each other for supremacy. In 1499, the French, allied to the city-state of Venice and backed by Pope Alexander VI, invaded Milan, ending Sforza's rule and causing Leonardo to flee the city. Two years before his departure, he had completed his painting of the *Last Supper* on a wall of a Milan convent. Most painters at that time applied the paint onto the plaster before it had dried, a technique known as fresco, which gave a **luminous** quality to the finished work. In contrast, Leonardo painted the *Last Supper* on dry plaster, using paints he had created. Although the painting began to deteriorate slightly even during Leonardo's lifetime, its dramatic composition and **sublime** spiritual quality have inspired awe in its viewers.

The second great work of art for which Leonardo is renowned is the portrait of a young woman whose **enigmatic** smile has intrigued people for centuries. This painting became known as the *Mona Lisa*. Leonardo painted it in 1503, following his return to Florence. Also dating from this period is a series of precise anatomical drawings made by Leonardo. At that time, knowledge of the workings of the human body was nonexistent. Doctors relied on centuries-old texts to treat disease, making medical treatment largely **ineffectual**. Leonardo obtained corpses from a Florence hospital and **dissected** over thirty of these in order to observe and make a record of their structure.

In 1513, Leonardo moved to Rome to work, but he often became so **mired** in thinking through and recording the ideas running through his mind that he did not complete very many projects. Francis I, the enlightened young king of France, invited Leonardo to his country where he remained the king's guest for the last two and a half years of his life. Out of gratitude, Leonardo gave the *Mona Lisa* to the young king. It has remained in France ever since, where it yearly attracts people from all over the world to view it in Paris's Louvre museum.

Answer each of the following questions in the form of a sentence. If a question does not contain a vocabulary word from this lesson's word list, use one in your answer. Use each word only once. Questions and answers will then contain all fifteen words (or forms of the words).

1. Why wasn't Milan a **congenial** place for Leonardo to be in 1499?

2. What evidence do we have of Leonardo's wide-ranging interests?

3. How does the passage indicate that we still do not know the reason for the *Mona Lisa's* smile?

4. What did da Vinci achieve in his painting of the *Last Supper?*

5. What effect does the fresco technique give to a mural?

6. Give approximate dates of the **millennium** known as the Middle Ages.

7. How did scholars **decipher** Leonardo's writings?

8. How do we know that Sforza's defense of Milan was **ineffectual**?

9. What is the meaning of **stagnated** as it is used in the passage?

10. Why was so little known about the human body during Leonardo's time?

11. Why did the ideas of the Greeks and Romans go unquestioned by most people?

12. Name one human quality that helped bring about the Renaissance.

13. How does the passage show that Francis I was not **mired** in the past?

14. What did people believe was the cause of the Black Death?

15. How would you describe the relationship between Milan and Venice?

FUN & FASCINATING FACTS

The Greek word for "fable" is *ainos,* and since the meaning of a fable has to be figured out, the verb *ainissesthai* came to mean "to speak in a puzzling way." From the Greek verb came the Latin *aenigma,* "a puzzling speech or riddle." Finally, the word passed into English as **enigma**, "anything that is puzzling or hard to figure out; a mystery."

~~~~~~~~~~

Millennium comes from the Latin words *mille,* "thousand," and *annus,* "year." The plural form is *millennia* or *millenniums.* The Latin *centum,* "one hundred," gives us *century,* "a period of one hundred years," and *decem,* "ten," gives us *decade,* "a period of ten years."

Millennium has a specialized meaning from the Book of Revelation, the last book of the Bible. Reference is made there to the anticipated reign of Christ on earth for a period of one thousand years. Christians refer to this period as "the millennium," and *millennium* has acquired in this way a secondary meaning, "a hoped for period of joy, peace, prosperity, and justice."

~~~~~~~~~~

The Latin for "swamp" is *stagnum* and gives us the verb **stagnate**. The water in a swamp does not flow; it *stagnates.* The adjective form is *stagnant.* The water in a swamp is *stagnant.*

Lesson 15

Word List
Study the definitions of the words below; then do the exercises for the lesson.

ascertain
as ər tān´

v. To find out for certain.
Ms. Jenckes sent Terry to **ascertain** the cause of the delay.

chastise
chas´ tīz

v. 1. To punish by beating.
A hundred years ago disruptive students were **chastised** with a cane.
2. To rebuke or criticize severely.
It is embarrassing to be **chastised** in public.

cull
kul

v. To select and remove weak or inferior members from.
Game wardens **cull** the deer herd when it grows too large for the food supply.

defer
dē fur´

v. 1. To put off or postpone.
General Rankin **deferred** a decision on moving troops forward until he heard from his scouts.
2. To yield to out of respect for the knowledge or authority of another.
My uncle usually **defers** to my aunt, who is a doctor, when someone in the family is sick.
deference *n.* (def´ ər əns) Submitting to the wishes of another because of respect.
Our parents taught my brother and me to show **deference** to our elders.

desist
di sist´

v. To refrain from continuing something.
Both sides must **desist** from shooting while their leaders meet to negotiate.

discredit
dis kred´ it

v. 1. To hurt the reputation of.
Mike was **discredited** by his own actions.
2. To destroy confidence or trust in.
New scientific evidence often **discredits** earlier theories.

encroach
en krōch´

v. To advance little by little beyond the usual limits or boundaries.
We pruned the branches of the maple tree that **encroached** on our property.

foreboding
fôr bōd´ iŋ

n. A strong feeling that something bad is about to happen.
It was with **foreboding** that we began to search for the missing child.

humane
hyo̅o̅ mān´

adj. Compassionate, kind to other human beings or to animals.
What is **humane** treatment for a horse with a broken leg?

irrational
ir rash´ ən əl

adj. Lacking sound judgment; not governed by reason.
As she approached the house, Candace felt an **irrational** fear inside herself.

lurid
lo̅or´ id

adj. 1. Causing horror; extremely gruesome.
My parents will not give me permission to see that movie because of several **lurid** scenes it contains.
2. Glowing with the redness of flames seen through a haze.
The dense smog gave the rays of the setting sun a **lurid** cast.

perpetuate
pər pech´ ōō āt

v. To cause to continue indefinitely.
The division of the country into sections for each religious group only **perpetuates** the hostility they feel toward each other.

restive
res´ tiv

adj. Showing impatience because of restrictions or delays.
We grew **restive** as we awaited permission to return to our flooded house.

stamina
stam´ ə nə

n. Physical strength or courage to resist hardship, illness, or fatigue.
Jill claims that running five miles a day has built up her **stamina**.

surveillance
sər vā´ ləns

n. Close observation of a person or area.
Because the police believed the suspect would contact his sister, they placed her under round-the-clock **surveillance**.

15A Finding Meanings

Choose two phrases to form a sentence that correctly uses a word from Word List 15. Write each sentence in the space provided.

1. (a) is to find out about it.   (c) is to keep it a secret.
   (b) To perpetuate something   (d) To ascertain something

2. (a) To discredit someone is to   (c) borrow from that person.
   (b) hurt that person's reputation. (d) To chastise someone is to

3. (a) one that is enjoying a rest period.   (c) one that is showing impatience.
   (b) A restive group is   (d) A humane group is

4. (a) a lack of certainty.   (c) a close watch on a subject.
   (b) Surveillance is   (d) Stamina is

5. (a) criticize that person severely. (c) To defer to someone is to
   (b) take that person's place.   (d) To chastise someone is to

6. (a) To perpetuate something   (c) To cull something
   (b) is to keep it going.   (d) is to put it out of one's mind.

7. (a) Foreboding is   (c) doubt about something.
   (b) Deference is   (d) respect shown to another.

ascertain
chastise
cull
defer
desist
discredit
encroach
foreboding
humane
irrational
lurid
perpetuate
restive
stamina
surveillance

8. (a) A lurid account   (c) is one that is highly critical.
   (b) An irrational account   (d) is one that shocks or horrifies.

9. (a) express one's feelings strongly.   (c) To encroach is to
   (b) refrain from continuing something.   (d) To desist is to

10. (a) Foreboding is   (c) an uneasy feeling about what might happen.
    (b) Stamina is   (d) the ability to predict future events.

15B Just the Right Word

Improve each of the following sentences by crossing out the bold phrase and replacing it with a word (or a form of the word) from Word List 15.

1. That **glowing reddish** light in the night sky was caused by a burning haystack.

2. How can we **find out for certain** the time that Doug left the house?

3. The large number of dropouts from our high school **shows that it is impossible to trust** this enthusiastic report on progress.

4. Swimming laps every morning builds up one's **ability to withstand fatigue**.

5. Keeping dogs in such small cages is not **treating them in a compassionate manner**.

6. The suburbs continue to **move little by little** onto good farmland.

7. Dairy farmers usually **select and sell** those cows that produce the least milk.

8. After a conference with my coach, I was willing to **yield out of respect** to his suggestions.

9. Everyone in the family worried that grandfather had been **quite incapable of thinking clearly and logically** when he sold his house without consulting any of them.

10. Airport officials insisted on **very close observation** of the baggage area at all times.

15C Applying Meanings

Circle the letter of each correct answer to the questions below. Questions may have more than one correct answer.

1. Which of the following can be **deferred**?
   - (a) a final decision
   - (b) payment
   - (c) the first day of spring
   - (d) one's retirement

2. Which of the following might fill one with **foreboding**?
   - (a) an anonymous threat
   - (b) a strange noise
   - (c) an affable employer
   - (d) a malevolent colleague

3. Which of the following can be **ascertained**?
   - (a) the price of a car
   - (b) the age of the earth
   - (c) the causes of the Civil War
   - (d) the weight of a diamond

4. Which of the following can be **irrational**?
   - (a) behavior
   - (b) people
   - (c) fear
   - (d) heat

5. Which of the following can be **lurid**?
   - (a) the sky
   - (b) a novel
   - (c) a dialect
   - (d) a fanfare

6. Which of the following might become **restive**?
   - (a) a loose boulder
   - (b) a bored audience
   - (c) an irksome task
   - (d) a small child

7. For which of the following would one need **stamina**?
   - (a) succumbing to a disease
   - (b) contemplating nature
   - (c) cycling across the country
   - (d) making a cake

8. Which of the following can be **discredited**?
   - (a) an explanation
   - (b) a rumor
   - (c) a claim
   - (d) a report

ascertain

chastise

cull

defer

desist

discredit

encroach

foreboding

humane

irrational

lurid

perpetuate

restive

stamina

surveillance

15D Word Study

Complete the analogies by selecting the pair of words whose relationship most resembles the relationship of the pair in capital letters. Circle the letter in front of the pair you choose.

1. MILLENNIUM : CENTURY ::
   (a) winter : summer
   (b) space : time
   (c) kilometer : mile
   (d) decade : year

2. PLEASANT : SUBLIME ::
   (a) plain : ornate
   (b) sore : excruciating
   (c) healthy : sick
   (d) brief : concise

3. SCOLD : CHASTISE ::
   (a) echo : reverberate
   (b) depart : embark
   (c) praise : lionize
   (d) increase : augment

4. PATIENT : RESTIVE ::
   (a) serene : turbulent
   (b) brief : concise
   (c) bizarre : inane
   (d) gruesome : grotesque

5. FOREBODING : MEMORY ::
   (a) claustrophobia : space
   (b) inkling : suspicion
   (c) future : past
   (d) imagination : reality

6. PERPETUATE : HALT ::
   (a) depict : illustrate
   (b) deter : discourage
   (c) encroach : withdraw
   (d) defer : yield

7. LUMINOUS : LIGHT ::
   (a) tasty : taste
   (b) audible : sound
   (c) sunny : day
   (d) starry : night

8. ENTHUSIASM : MANIA ::
   (a) serenity : turmoil
   (b) defiance : mutiny
   (c) doctor : patient
   (d) health : pestilence

9. CONGENIAL : SMILE ::
   (a) contagious : disease
   (b) ardent : ardor
   (c) synonymous : name
   (d) angry : frown

10. BARTER : GOODS ::
    (a) exchange : greetings
    (b) create : art
    (c) play : sports
    (d) perform : audience

Read the passage below; then complete the exercise that follows.

Who's Afraid of the Big, Bad Wolf?

Early American settlers, alone at night in their log cabins, far from their nearest neighbors, must have had a sense of **foreboding** as they heard the howling of wolves in the darkness. **Lurid** stories of savage attacks on humans had fired their imaginations, while phrases such as "keeping the wolf from the door," along with tales like "Little Red Riding Hood," may have **perpetuated** the belief that the wolf was a ferocious beast who made unprovoked attacks on humans.

This fear of wolves is quite **irrational**. Wolves do kill to live, but they do not kill humans. Every story of a wolf attacking humans has been **discredited** by those who have studied the subject. One researcher investigating the behavior of arctic wolves in northern Canada removed a pup from its mother and took it into a nearby tent. Even though the mother became **restive**, she waited outside the tent until the pup was returned to her.

The truth is that wolves are quite wary, if not completely afraid, of humans and with good reason. During the last several hundred years, humans have **encroached** on their habitats and by trapping, shooting, and poisoning have almost completely eliminated them from the lower forty-eight states. Today, the gray wolf, also known as the timber wolf, is found on the North American continent only in the northern United States and Canada.

In the last several decades, however, attitudes toward wolves have been changing. As people have understood that these creatures might not survive without human help, they have actively supported plans to reestablish wolves in wilderness areas where they once flourished. During the late 1980s, red wolves were successfully returned to regions of the southeastern United States where they once lived. In 1995, a three-year project to reintroduce gray wolves to one of their original habitats began in Yellowstone National Park.

To make sure these projects succeed, scientists and wildlife specialists have been studying wolves extensively. To gather information, they catch individual animals in **humane** traps, then fit them with collars containing radio transmitters before releasing them. These transmitters help the scientists **ascertain** the movements of wolf packs. Other observers keep the animals under **surveillance** from aircraft flying overhead.

From their observations, scientists know that a wolf pack usually consists of five to fifteen animals and may need anywhere from forty to four hundred square miles in order to maintain itself, the size depending on the number of wolves in the pack and the amount of game available. In their continual search for food, wolves demonstrate tremendous **stamina**, maintaining a steady pace for hours at a time if necessary. They show amazing intelligence as they work in close cooperation with each other to bring down their prey, which includes elk, moose, caribou, and deer. By **culling** herds of old or sick animals, wolves perform a valuable service, strengthening the herd by leaving more grazing areas for the remaining animals. If a herd becomes much reduced, wolves will **desist** from preying on it until its size has increased to a normal level.

Wolves usually mate for life. They are very protective of their young, caring for them until they are fully grown at about two years. A strict social order is maintained within the pack and all **defer** to the leader, who alone decides when and where to hunt.

Scientists have observed that wolves communicate in various ways. Whimpering indicates restlessness or hunger, while snarling is used to put members of the pack in their place if they become too assertive, almost like a parent **chastising** an unruly child. As for the howling in the night that struck terror into the American settlers' hearts, it was probably a warning to other wolves that their scent had been detected and that they were invading territory that was already occupied. It did not mean that an attack on humans was imminent. As a Canadian trapper is once supposed to have said: "Anyone who says he's been et by a wolf is a liar."

Answer each of the following questions in the form of a sentence. If a question does not contain a vocabulary word from this lesson's word list, use one in your answer. Use each word only once. Questions and answers will then contain all fifteen words (or forms of the words).

1. How do wolves keep herds of deer and other animals healthy?

2. How have the actions of humans toward wolves changed in the last twenty years?

3. What is the meaning of **discredited** as it is used in the passage?

4. How might the mother wolf who had her pup taken away have communicated that she was **restive**?

5. Why would it be inaccurate to describe the social order in a wolf pack as equal?

6. Why would it be **irrational** to fear wolves today?

7. What is the meaning of **chastise** as it is used in the passage?

8. Why were people's **forebodings** unnecessary when they heard wolves howl?

9. How do researchers **ascertain** information about wolves today?

10. Why do you think **surveillance** of wolf pack movements would be easier in winter?

11. Why are tales like "Little Red Riding Hood" unfair to wolves?

12. What is the meaning of **lurid** as it is used in the passage?

13. What is one possible reason for wolves howling?

14. What is required of a **humane** trap for catching wolves?

15. What physical quality do wolves have that makes them good hunters?

FUN & FASCINATING FACTS

One very well-known line of poetry is Alexander Pope's "To err is human, to forgive divine." However, what he actually wrote was, "To err is humane, to forgive divine." In the early eighteenth century, when the line was written, *human* and **humane** did not have separate meanings. This is no longer the case. *Human* refers to any quality—good, bad, or neutral—associated with human beings. (The *human* voice has a range of about two octaves.) *Humane* is restricted to those qualities that express sympathy for other creatures. (The law requires the *humane* treatment of animals in captivity.)

In Greek mythology, the three fates were goddesses who controlled the length of human life. They were Clotho, who spun the thread of life; Lachesis, who measured its length; and Atropos, who cut it. The Greek word for thread is *stemon*, which passed into Latin as *stamen*, the plural of which is **stamina**. Those who lived a long time were believed to have lengthy *stamina*, or "threads of life." Because people who lived to an old age were believed to have physical strength and endurance, *stamina* came to have these meanings. Note that although *stamina* is a plural form in Latin, in English *stamina* is treated as a singular noun.

Lesson 16

Word List
Study the definitions of the words below; then do the exercises for the lesson.

alleviate
ə lē´ vē āt
v. To relieve or make more bearable.
Gargling with salt water **alleviates** a sore throat.

antidote
an´ ti dōt
n. 1. A remedy that relieves the effects of a poison.
The correct **antidote** for cyanide poisoning is sodium nitrite.
2. Anything that offers relief from an undesirable condition.
Her surprise birthday party was an **antidote** to Anzi's losing the tennis match.

bedlam
bed´ ləm
n. A very confused and noisy scene.
Bedlam broke out on the factory floor when the plant's closing was announced.

cajole
kə jōl´
v. To urge with gentle and repeated requests; to coax.
Jillian allowed herself to be **cajoled** into acting as class treasurer.

glib
glib
adj. Marked by an ease in speaking or writing that often shows lack of concern or sincerity.
The candidate's **glib** responses to questions made it difficult to understand his opinion about raising taxes.

haggard
hag´ ərd
adj. Having a tired look; worn out.
The **haggard** faces of the refugees spoke of many fear-filled days and sleepless nights.

immaculate
i mak´ yo͞o lət
adj. 1. Perfectly clean; spotless.
The dining room's white linen tablecloths were starched and **immaculate** at the beginning of the reception.
2. Without a flaw; faultless.
Her automobile insurance premiums were reduced due to her **immaculate** driving record.

incessant
in ses´ ənt
adj. Going on without interruption; continual.
Last night, we hardly slept because of the **incessant** noise from the apartment downstairs.

indulgent
in dul´ jənt
adj. Inclined to give in easily; lenient.
The **indulgent** parents bought their son almost every computer game that he asked for.
indulge *v.* 1. To give in too easily to the wishes of.
My grandparents loved to **indulge** my brothers and me when they came to visit.
2. To yield to.
I **indulged** my craving for something sweet by having an ice-cream cone.

loll
läl
v. 1. To sit back in a relaxed way; to sprawl.
I **lolled** in the hammock for most of that humid summer afternoon.
2. To hang loosely; to droop.
After the storm, the seasick passenger's head **lolled** over the rail of the ship.

pittance
pit´ ns
n. A very small amount, especially of money.
The manager had a difficult time keeping employees because the job paid only a **pittance**.

pungent
pun´ jənt

adj. 1. Having a sharp taste or smell.
A **pungent** sauce of pineapple and ginger was served over the pork.
2. Sharply critical; painfully direct.
The newspaper editorial contained **pungent** criticism of the committee's proposed cuts in the city's education budget.

rue
roō

v. To feel regret or sorrow over.
After his outburst, he immediately **rued** his angry words.

strident
strīd´ nt

adj. Harsh and grating; loud and shrill.
The counselor's **strident** voice awakened the campers every morning.

vehement
vē´ ə mənt

adj. Expressing strong feeling; intense.
Their differing political beliefs sometimes caused **vehement** arguments between the friends.

16A Finding Meanings

Choose two phrases to form a sentence that correctly uses a word from Word List 16. Write each sentence in the space provided.

1. (a) A pittance is
   (b) a plea for understanding.
   (c) A bedlam is
   (d) a confused and noisy place.

2. (a) keep trying to persuade that person.
   (b) feel sorry for that person.
   (c) To indulge someone is to
   (d) To cajole someone is to

3. (a) Glib appeals are those
   (b) that go on repeatedly.
   (c) that go unanswered.
   (d) Incessant appeals are those

4. (a) a remedy for something harmful.
   (b) An antidote is
   (c) A pittance is
   (d) an expression of sorrow or regret.

5. (a) To loll on something is to
   (b) To rue something is to
   (c) rely on it.
   (d) lie back in a relaxed way on it.

6. (a) makes excessive demands.
   (b) gives in to requests very easily.
   (c) An immaculate employer is one who
   (d) An indulgent relative is one who

alleviate
antidote
bedlam
cajole
glib
haggard
immaculate
incessant
indulgent
loll
pittance
pungent
rue
strident
vehement

7. (a) A glib denial is one
   (b) made in a hesitant manner.
   (c) A vehement denial is one
   (d) made with passionate intensity.

8. (a) have a guilty expression.
   (b) To be immaculate is to
   (c) be without a flaw.
   (d) To be strident is to

9. (a) To alleviate something is to
   (b) make it less bothersome.
   (c) make it worse.
   (d) To rue something is to

10. (a) A pungent comment is one
    (b) that is meant to soothe.
    (c) A strident comment is one
    (d) that is sharply critical.

16B Just the Right Word

Improve each of the following sentences by crossing out the bold phrase and replacing it with a word (or a form of the word) from Word List 16.

1. Jenny could afford few luxuries on the **very small amount of money** she made at her job.

2. I now **feel deep regret over** my decision to delay studying until the day before the test.

3. I drew back from the open jar of salsa because the smell of the chili pepper was so **sharp and strong**.

4. The farmer warned us about the insecticide by reminding us that there is no **substance that can be used as a remedy** for it.

5. "Her white dress will not stay **spotlessly clean** for long," thought the child's nursemaid as they left for the birthday party.

6. The agent's **smoothly spoken but insincere** assurances didn't convince me that my suitcases would follow me as I changed planes.

7. The **loud and high-pitched** cries of gulls fighting over scraps rose from the dock.

8. The climbers looked **as if they had endured great hardship** after they'd spent three days on the mountain in a snowstorm.

9. The dog's tongue **hung loosely** from its mouth on that sweltering summer afternoon.

10. When Aunt Bettina comes to visit each year, she enjoys **readily granting the requests of** her favorite niece.

16C Applying Meanings

Circle the letter of each correct answer to the questions below. Questions may have more than one correct answer.

1. Which of the following adjectives would not describe a **bedlam**?

  (a) sweltering   (c) humdrum

  (b) serene   (d) tumultuous

2. Which of the following might make a person look **haggard**?

  (a) lack of sleep   (c) worry

  (b) illness   (d) prudence

3. For which of the following might there be an **antidote**?

  (a) a poison   (c) a snake bite

  (b) anxiety   (d) serenity

4. Which of the following could be a **pittance**?

  (a) a small favor   (c) a short distance

  (b) a sum of money   (d) a weekly wage

5. Which of the following can be **pungent**?

  (a) a panorama   (c) a rock

  (b) an aroma   (d) a comment

6. Which of the following might a person **rue**?

  (a) speaking rudely   (c) joining a conspiracy

  (b) heeding sage advice   (d) making an inane suggestion

7. Which of the following can be **glib**?

  (a) an endeavor   (c) a speech

  (b) an argument   (d) a manner of walking

8. Which of the following might be **indulged**?

  (a) a desire   (c) a child

  (b) a legacy   (d) a tirade

alleviate

antidote

bedlam

cajole

glib

haggard

immaculate

incessant

indulgent

loll

pittance

pungent

rue

strident

vehement

16D Word Study

Each group of four words below contains two words that are either synonyms or antonyms. Circle these two words, then circle the *S* if they are synonyms, the *A* if they are antonyms.

1. mild	vehement	despicable	glib	S	A
2. fitful	contagious	immaculate	filthy	S	A
3. relieve	alleviate	cajole	dread	S	A
4. loll	sprawl	retire	deter	S	A
5. coax	indulge	regret	cajole	S	A
6. glib	incessant	awkward	enigmatic	S	A
7. lenient	synonymous	anonymous	indulgent	S	A
8. miser	philanthropist	artisan	connoisseur	S	A
9. accede	immerse	consent	conjecture	S	A
10. strident	humdrum	meticulous	electrifying	S	A

16E Passage

Read the passage below; then complete the exercise that follows.

The Wisdom of Rabbi Rabinowicz

The Jewish people long ago discovered that humor can be an **antidote** for hardship, and this fact is reflected in many of their folk tales. The following story from Russia tells of Moishe, a hardworking but poor tailor, and his wife Sarah. Did I say poor? Truth to tell, Moishe's business brought in barely enough money to pay the rent on their small house and put food on their table.

Moishe's brother Jacob and sister-in-law Martha lived in the next village with their six children. Jacob worked as a roofer, but his earnings never amounted to more than a **pittance**, for—as he never tired of explaining—a roofer can't work in the rain, and when it isn't raining, who needs roof repairs?

One day Jacob came to his brother with a plea for help. He and his family had been evicted from their home and needed a place to stay. Of course, it would be just for a short time. Moishe sympathized with his brother but explained that his house was barely big enough for two. How would eight more people fit into it? But Jacob, though an indifferent roofer, was a **glib** talker. In no time, he had **cajoled** his brother into offering temporary shelter.

Moishe and Sarah felt that their home had been invaded by a small army. The children were allowed to run wild because Jacob and Martha were the most **indulgent** of parents, never correcting them. Their muddy boots trampled dirt all over the floor, and the house, which once had been **immaculate**, became impossible to keep clean. Jacob spent the whole day **lolling** in Moishe's favorite armchair, while Martha's **strident** voice never seemed to need a rest.

Sarah **rued** the day her husband had invited his relatives into their home. As for Moishe himself, he could scarcely sleep at night. When he grew increasingly **haggard,** Sarah became so worried that she sent her husband to Rabbi Rabinowicz for guidance. The rabbi's advice was simple. Knowing that Moishe kept a couple of goats and some hens in his backyard, he told the exhausted man to move the animals into the house. Moishe was puzzled. He could not imagine how such an action would **alleviate** the problem, but since the rabbi was known for his sage counsel, Moishe felt it was not his place to raise objections. Sarah, who had no such qualms, argued **vehemently** against the plan. In the end, neither one was willing to disregard completely the rabbi's recommendation, so they brought the goats and the hens into the house.

If things had been bad before, they were now ten times worse. The hens' **incessant** cackling nearly drove Moishe out of his mind, and the **pungent** odors of the goats were sickening. Poor Moishe's home was in such a **bedlam** that any thought of sleep was impossible. In tears, he returned to the rabbi to ask what to do. The rabbi told him to return the goats and the chickens to the backyard.

Moishe's relief was enormous as he drove the squawking chickens and the stubborn goats out of his house. The rooms suddenly seemed so peaceful that he scarcely noticed the unruly children, his loud-mouthed sister-in-law, and his good-for-nothing brother.

"Peace," he murmured, "it's wonderful! That Rabbi Rabinowicz is a genius."

Answer each of the following questions in the form of a sentence. If a question does not contain a vocabulary word from this lesson's word list, use one in your answer. Use each word only once. Questions and answers will then contain all fifteen words (or forms of the words).

1. How do you know that Jacob made very little money as a roofer?

2. Why was Jacob able to talk his brother into letting him move in?

3. Why do you think much Jewish humor deals with hardship?

4. Why might it have been unpleasant to listen to Martha?

5. Why was Moishe becoming more and more **haggard**?

6. What is the meaning of **pungent** as it is used in the passage?

7. Why is it inaccurate to say that Sarah was happy to have her brother-in-law's family staying in her home?

8. Why was it impossible to escape the sound of Martha's voice?

9. How do we know that Moishe did not agree right away to Jacob's request?

10. What is the meaning of **immaculate** as it is used in the passage?

11. How did Moishe **indulge** his brother?

12. What is the meaning of **lolling** as it is used in the passage?

13. What seemed to **alleviate** the confusion and noise in Moishe's home?

14. What was Sarah's view of the rabbi's plan?

15. What are some details from the passage that illustrate that **bedlam** reigned in Moishe's home after the arrival of his brother's family?

FUN & FASCINATING FACTS

The Greek prefix *anti-* (meaning "opposite" or "against") combines with the Greek root *dosis* (meaning "something given") to form **antidote**. Note that *antidote* may be followed by *to* (a good book is an antidote *to* boredom), by *for* (an antidote *for* snakebite), and by *against* (friendship as an antidote *against* loneliness). If you confuse this word with *anecdote* (meaning "a short, interesting, or amusing story of some happening or about a person"), you might be called a Mrs. Malaprop.

Mrs. Malaprop is a character in a play called *The Rivals* by the eighteenth-century playwright Richard Brinsley Sheridan. She elicits laughter in the theater by confusing words that are similar in sound but different in meaning. She is the sort of person who says she is going to tell you an amusing *antidote* or offer you what she would call an *anecdote* for a bee sting. Such a misuse of words is called a *malapropism*.

The Hospital of Saint Mary of Bethlehem in London was for several centuries a kind of prison for the severely mentally ill. In those days there was no effective treatment for such people. As a result, the "hospital" was a very noisy place, filled with confusion and tumult. Over time, the hospital's name was shortened to Bedlam. The "hospital" is long gone, but the word **bedlam**, meaning a condition of noise and confusion, remains.

Review for Lessons 13–16

Hidden Message In the boxes provided, write the words from Lessons 13 through 16 that are missing in each of the sentences below. The number following each sentence gives the word list from which the missing word is taken. When the exercise is finished, the shaded boxes should spell out a definition from the "Devil's Dictionary" of Ambrose Bierce, the American writer who was born in 1842 and disappeared while traveling in Mexico in 1913.

1. Three nights without sleep left him looking _____ . (16)

2. His _____ answers suggested a lack of seriousness. (16)

3. Grandma told me just to _____ in her armchair. (16)

4. Her _____ for fashion design got her the job. (13)

5. My voice could not be heard above the _____ . (16)

6. The _____ killed thousands before it ended. (14)

7. A stern look was enough to _____ the child. (15)

8. We must either make progress or _____ . (14)

9. I could not _____ the scrawled message. (14)

10. I will _____ to your better judgment. (15)

11. Their dishonesty _____ the company. (15)

12. The horses grew _____ before the thunderstorm. (15)

13. She tried to _____ me into going with her. (16)

14. Her _____ comments showed her disapproval. (16)

15. The committee proceeded despite the _____ objections of some members. (16)

16. Stars are _____ objects in the night sky. (14)

17. The _____ cries of seagulls filled the air. (16)

18. Let's not _____ over how much each of us will pay. (13)

19. We've had enough; please _____ from bothering us. (15)

20. Exercise is a good _____ to stress. (16)

21. Her chief _____ is the family home. (13)

22. Stepping on the scale will _____ me from overeating while on vacation. (13)

23. A sharp knife is needed to _____ the specimen. (14)

24. Filled with _____ , we nervously awaited the results. (15)

25. The land purchase proved to be a(n) _____ for the city. (13)

26. Talking to plants seems to be a(n) _____ act. (15)

27. The comic had a(n) _____ for making children laugh. (13)

28. The child took advantage of the _____ baby sitter. (16)

29. She is an expert on the _____ writings of Shakespeare. (14)

30. A sprinter needs speed rather than _____ . (15)

31. Measles and mumps are highly _____. (13)

32. The shelter cared for pets in a(n) _____ manner. (15)

33. I _____ the day I agreed to take care of her pets. (16)

34. Although the pay was a(n) _____ , I liked the work. (16)

35. Our neighbors said that their garden would not _____ on our property. (15)

36. The _____ glow in the sky came from a chemical fire. (15)

37. The children's _____ for Sudoku mystified Grandad. (13)

38. The poet's identity is a(n) _____ to this day. (14)

39. His objections will not _____ our plans. (13)

40. Clouds of mosquitoes began to _____ us. (13)

41. Do you _____ making any further changes? (13)

42. We will never _____ what really happened. (15)

43. You _____ your deposit if you don't complete the deal. (13)

44. Mom will _____ the smallest tomato plants. (15)

45. Aspirin should _____ a headache. (16)

46. _____ rains kept us indoors. (16)

47. This award will _____ the benefactor's name. (15)

48. Colleges _____ to attract the best students. (14)

49. He's a(n) _____ believer in vigorous exercise. (13)

Lesson 17

Word List

Study the definitions of the words below; then do the exercises for the lesson.

accord
ə kôrd´

n. A feeling of agreement or harmony; a formal agreement.
The members of the jury were in **accord** when the vote was taken.

affirm
ə fʉrm´

v. To declare positively.
This official will **affirm** that the signature is mine.

bequeath
bē kwēth

v. 1. To pass on to others.
Through his pamphlet *Common Sense*, Thomas Paine **bequeathed** a concern for individual rights and freedom to future generations.
2. To leave to another in one's will.
This stamp collection was **bequeathed** to me by my father.
bequest *n.* (bē kwest´) Something bequeathed; a legacy.
The will contains a **bequest** of a thousand dollars to a friendly neighbor.

citadel
sit´ ə dəl

n. A fortress on a hill; a stronghold.
The old section of Quebec City is surrounded by walls and dominated by a **citadel**.

confer
kən fʉr´

v. 1. To grant or bestow.
The college president **conferred** the degree of Bachelor of Arts upon the students who had completed the four-year course of study.
2. To consult.
The surgeon **conferred** with her colleague before deciding not to operate on the patient.

coup
kōo

n. 1. A successful action that brings about a striking change.
Hiring violinist Itzhak Perlman for the festival was a **coup** for the music director.
2. The overthrow of a government, especially by a group that has military or political power.
In 1952, a **coup** in Egypt forced the king out of power and led the way to presidential leadership for that country.

dignitary
dig´ ni ter ē

n. A person who holds a high rank or position of honor.
Dignitaries from the United Nations attended the White House dinner.

embroil
em broil´

v. To involve in an argument or conflict.
The two countries were **embroiled** in a bitter dispute over where the border between them lay.

epoch
ep´ ək

n. An extended period of time marked by a series of related events.
The **epoch** known as the Cold War, a period of hostility without military conflict between the United States and the Soviet Union, began around 1945 and ended in 1991.

impeccable
im pek´ ə bəl

adj. Free from fault or flaw; perfect.
The ballet dancer's **impeccable** execution of a midair turn elicited cries of "Bravo!" from the audience.

institute in´ stə tōōt	*v.* To establish, organize, or put into effect; to begin. The proprietor **instituted** important changes in employee benefits when she bought the business. *n.* An organization set up to promote education or a particular cause. Scholars at the **Institute** for Advanced Study in Princeton, New Jersey, conduct research in mathematics, physics, and historical and social sciences.
patriarch pā´ trē ärk	*n.* The male founder or ruler of a family or tribe. The Bedouins, nomadic desert tribes of Arabia, form extended families headed by **patriarchs**.
rapport ra pôr´	*n.* A feeling of harmonious connection between people or groups of people. Successful speakers quickly establish a **rapport** with the audience.
renounce rē nouns´	*v.* To give up a right to, abandon; reject. We **renounced** meat eating when we became vegetarians. **renunciation** *n.* (rē nun sē ā´ shən) The act of renouncing. Acceptance into the monastery required the **renunciation** of the use of alcoholic beverages.
rhetoric ret´ ər ik	*n.* 1. The art of using language skillfully. We studied **rhetoric** to improve our debating skills. 2. Exaggerated or insincere language that is without real meaning or worth. Because it offered no practical solutions to inner-city housing problems, the mayor's speech was mere **rhetoric**.

17A Finding Meanings

Choose two phrases to form a sentence that correctly uses a word from Word List 17. Write each sentence in the space provided.

1. (a) something that is handed down.
   (b) An accord is
   (c) A bequest is
   (d) a change of direction.

2. (a) A patriarch is
   (b) A dignitary is
   (c) a person with great strength.
   (d) the male leader of a tribe.

3. (a) a type of car.
   (b) a formal agreement.
   (c) A coup is
   (d) An accord is

4. (a) one who speaks eloquently.
   (b) one who holds a position of honor.
   (c) A dignitary is
   (d) A citadel is

5. (a) Rhetoric is
   (b) Rapport is
   (c) an opportunity to make a difference.
   (d) skill in the use of language.

6. (a) a fortress.
   (b) a beginning.
   (c) An institute is
   (d) A citadel is

7. (a) a poem that relates a story.
   (b) an action that brings about a striking change.
   (c) A coup is
   (d) An epoch is

8. (a) To renounce an award is to
   (b) To confer an award is to
   (c) grant it.
   (d) accept it.

9. (a) something left to a person in a will.
   (b) an organization to promote a particular cause.
   (c) An epoch is
   (d) An institute is

10. (a) to declare it to be true.
    (b) To affirm something is
    (c) To renounce something is
    (d) to go in search of it.

17B Just the Right Word

Improve each of the following sentences by crossing out the bold phrase and replacing it with a word (or a form of the word) from Word List 17.

accord
affirm
bequeath
citadel
confer
coup
dignitary
embroil
epoch
impeccable
institute
patriarch
rapport
renounce
rhetoric

1. The supervisor and the programmer had a good **feeling of emotional connection** with each other.

2. In 1981, Andreas Papandreou became prime minister of Greece by using **elaborate and ostentatious language** containing anti-Western ideas designed to appeal to voters.

3. Before he was overthrown by Castro in 1959, the dictator Batista controlled Cuba as a result of the **seizure of government** he staged in 1952.

4. My grandmother **put in her will that she wished to leave** this gold locket to me.

5. The judges at the figure-skating competition **had a discussion** at great length before announcing the winner.

6. In 1936, King Edward VIII of England **gave up his right to** the throne in order to marry a divorced American, Mrs. Wallis Simpson.

7. The United States did not officially become **caught up in the conflict** in World War Two until after the Japanese attack on the Pacific Fleet in Pearl Harbor in 1941.

8. The principal **set into motion** a policy that would discourage unnecessary absences at the high school.

9. Her behavior was **free of any fault** while she was with me.

10. With the death of Stalin, leader of the USSR (Union of Soviet Socialist Republics) from 1924 to 1953, came the end of a(n) **period of time marked by a series of related events** in Russian history.

17C Applying Meanings

Circle the letter of each correct answer to the questions below. Question may have more than one correct answer.

1. Which of the following might be **bequeathed**?
   - (a) a sum of money
   - (b) a work of art
   - (c) a piece of property
   - (d) a belief in democracy

2. Which of the following can be **conferred**?
   - (a) a gift
   - (b) a love of freedom
   - (c) one's innocence
   - (d) a title

3. Which of the following would be in **accord**?
   - (a) parties to an agreement
   - (b) rivals
   - (c) advocates for opposing views
   - (d) signers of a declaration

4. Which of the following is an **institute**?
   - (a) the Academy of Arts
   - (b) the Astrological Society
   - (c) the Depot Restaurant
   - (d) the American Civil Liberties Union

5. Which of the following might indicate **rapport** between two people?
   - (a) an affable exchange of views
   - (b) a rebuke of one by the other
   - (c) turmoil in their relationship
   - (d) constant wrangling between them

6. Which of the following occupations requires skill in **rhetoric**?
   - (a) lawyer
   - (b) dentist
   - (c) sales manager
   - (d) football coach

7. Which of the following is an **epoch**?
   - (a) the year 2000
   - (b) the Space Age
   - (c) the Middle Ages
   - (d) one's high school years

8. Which of the following is a **dignitary**?
   - (a) the president of a college
   - (b) the head of a conspiracy
   - (c) the president of a country
   - (d) the head of a household

17D Word Study

Fill in the blank spaces using prefixes and roots from the lists below.

Use these prefixes:

ad- (to)   *con-* (with)   *dis-* (apart)

im- (not)   *in-* (not)   *syn-* (together)

Form roots from these Latin words:

cessare (to cease)   *onuma* (name)   *ardere* (to burn)   *lumen* (light)

levis (light)   *macula* (stain)   *mille* (thousand)   *stagnum* (swamp)

annus (year)   *secare* (to cut)   *tangere* (to touch)

1. The prefix *ad-* combines with the root from *levis* to form the word _____ , "to make lighter or less burdensome."

2. Roots from the Latin word *mille* and *annus* combine to form _____ , "a period of a thousand years."

3. The prefix *con-* combines with the root from *tangere* to form _____ , "easily passed from person to person."

4. The prefix *in-* combines with the root from *cessare* to form _____ , "going on without ceasing."

5. The prefix *im-* combines with the root from *macula* to form _____ , "without a stain; spotless."

6. The prefix *syn-* combines with the root from *onuma* to form _____ , "closely related; linked together."

7. The word _____ means "burning with enthusiasm" and comes from the Latin *ardere*.

8. The word _____ means "giving off light" and comes from the Latin *lumen*.

9. The prefix *dis-* combines with the root from *secare* to form _____ , "to cut into in order to study."

10. The word _____ means "not changing" and comes from the Latin *stagnum*.

accord

affirm

bequeath

citadel

confer

coup

dignitary

embroil

epoch

impeccable

institute

patriarch

rapport

renounce

rhetoric

17E Passage

Read the passage below; then complete the exercise that follows.

The Country Without an Army

At the close of the ceremony honoring him, the dark-haired, **impeccably** dressed forty-six-year-old passed among the many **dignitaries** gathered at San José's Metropolitan Cathedral and embraced a frail, elderly man who had tears of joy streaming down his cheeks. On this occasion, Costa Ricans had gathered to celebrate their president Oscar Arias Sánchez, who was about to leave for Oslo to receive the 1987 Nobel Prize for Peace.

This award was to be **conferred** upon Arias because he was the main architect of an **accord**, known as "The Arias Peace Plan," signed that year by representatives from Nicaragua, Guatemala, Costa Rica, El Salvador, and Honduras. It **affirmed** the intentions of these countries to make a strong effort to end the armed conflict that had **embroiled** parts of Central America for decades. Arias was uniquely qualified to initiate this effort; for almost forty years his country had enjoyed both domestic tranquility and a democratic political system. Both of these blessings had been **bequeathed** to Costa Rica by its former president José Figueres Ferrer, the man Arias now embraced.

In the early 1940s, Figueres was a successful but largely unknown coffee planter. Outraged by the country's corrupt government, which, like those that had preceded it, rigged elections, shot or jailed political opponents, and allowed the army to brutalize the population into abject submission, Figueres gave a radio speech in 1942 attacking the country's president. For this act, he was sent into exile, but his courageous defiance made him a national hero. Six years later, he led an armed **coup** that toppled the government.

The year 1948 marked the beginning of a new **epoch** in Costa Rican history. The new government that Figueres formed in May of that year transformed Costa Rica in the first few months of its existence. Among the reforms he **instituted** were full voting rights for women, low-cost health care, and free and open elections. But his most amazing accomplishment was the **renunciation** of war. This was not mere **rhetoric**. He followed up his declaration by abolishing Costa Rica's army and taking a sledge hammer to strike the symbolic blow that began the destruction of the army's headquarters. As head of the National Liberation Party, which he formed, Figueres was three times elected president of his country, an indication of the strong **rapport** that existed between the citizens and this leader.

Now, in 1987, the aged Costa Rican **patriarch** stood on the steps of the Metropolitan Cathedral with the younger man now carrying Figueres's dream of peace beyond the nation's frontiers. The former and current presidents acknowledged the cheers of the people as they made their way on foot, and without need of protection, to the National Museum of Culture, once the site of the **citadel**, headquarters for the army. Having observed all this, an onlooker commented, "It was as though George Washington had appeared at the inauguration of John F. Kennedy."

Answer each of the following questions in the form of a sentence. If a question does not contain a vocabulary word from this lesson's word list, use one in your answer. Use each word only once. Questions and answers will then contain all fifteen words (or forms of the words).

1. What ended for Costa Rica in 1948?

2. How did the Costa Rican people **affirm** their respect for Figueres and Arias?

3. Was there anything unseemly about Arias's record as president of Costa Rica? Explain.

4. What is the meaning of **rhetoric** as it is used in the passage?

5. In what way can José Figueres be compared to George Washington?

6. How has Costa Rica gotten along with its neighbors in recent decades?

7. Give evidence of the **rapport** between Figueres and the people of Costa Rica.

8. Why is the Arias Peace Plan described as an **accord**?

9. Name some of Figueres's **bequests** to Costa Rica.

10. How did Figueres come to power in Costa Rica?

11. What is the meaning of **conferred** as it is used in the passage?

12. Which **dignitaries** signed the Arias Peace Plan?

13. What is the name of the **institute** that celebrates Costa Rican culture?

14. What did the signers of the Arias Peace Plan pledge to **renounce**?

15. Why would the army have had its headquarters in a **citadel**?

FUN & FASCINATING FACTS

If, after having a "heart-to-heart" talk with someone, you find yourselves in complete agreement, you could say that you are in **accord** with each other. This would be particularly appropriate since the word is formed from the Latin prefix *ad-*, meaning "to," and the Latin root *cor*, meaning "heart." Other English words derived from this same Latin root include *courage* (To put heart into someone is to give that person courage), *cordial* (A hearty welcome is similar to one that is cordial), and *cardiac* (A person goes into cardiac arrest when the heart suddenly stops beating).

In French *coup* means "blow" or "strike." *Coup* in English, meaning "the overthrow of a government," is short for the French *coup d'état* (pronounced koō dā tä´), meaning "a sudden blow within the state."

A *coupe* (pronounced koōp) is a closed, two-door automobile. A *coop* (also pronounced koōp) is a shed where hens are kept.

The adjective form of **rhetoric** is *rhetorical*. A *rhetorical* question is one that is asked only for effect and does not require an answer. *What sort of person would betray his country for a few dollars?* is a rhetorical question.

Lesson 18

Word List

Study the definitions of the words below; then do the exercises for the lesson.

aperture
ap´ ər chər

n. An opening or hole.
Tony could see an eye peering at him through a small **aperture** in the door.

cache
kash

n. 1. A hiding or storage place, especially for food or valuables.
A hollowed-out book provided a **cache** for the family's jewels.
2. Anything hidden or stored in such a place.
I found my sister's **cache** of marbles in the back of the closet.

combustible
kəm bus´ ti bəl

adj. Capable of catching fire or burning.
Don't store **combustible** rags near the furnace.

delegate
del´ ə gət

n. A person appointed to act on behalf of others; a representative.
Delegates from each section of the state attended the meeting on water conservation in the capital.
v. (del´ ə gāt) To assign or entrust to another.
Mr. Reese **delegated** to Karen and me the task of lining up the music for our school dance.

inclement
in klem´ ənt

adj. 1. Stormy.
We had such **inclement** weather on the scheduled day of our field trip to the zoo that we postponed it to the following week.
2. Harsh; not merciful.
The warden's decision to shackle the prisoners was only one of his many **inclement** actions.

indelible
in del´ ə bəl

adj. Not able to be erased; permanent.
The beauty of Venice made an **indelible** impression on the visitors.

malady
mal´ ə dē

n. A sickness or unhealthy condition.
Malaria is a **malady** prevalent in tropical areas.

memoir
mem´ wär

n. An account based on the author's personal experiences.
The Civil War anthology contains a moving **memoir** by a young Union cavalry officer.

paramount
par´ ə mount

adj. Most important; chief.
It is **paramount** that my mother receive this message before she leaves the house at 5:00 P.M.

rectify
rek´ tə fī

v. To correct or adjust.
The hospital **rectified** the mistake in billing by sending Uncle Guy a check for the amount he had overpaid.

requisite
rek´ wə zit

adj. Required; necessary.
When Aunt Mercedes completes the **requisite** two-year course, she plans to become a travel agent.
n. Something that is required or necessary.
Our Italian teacher always insisted that a sharp pencil and a sharp mind were the two **requisites** for taking a test.

146

squeamish
skwēm´ ish

adj. Easily made to feel upset or sick to the stomach.
There is no reason to feel **squeamish** about giving blood.

tract
trakt

n. 1. An area of land or water.
The students developed a **tract** of land in the center of the city for a vegetable garden.
2. A system of organs in the body that performs some function together.
The esophagus and stomach are part of the digestive **tract**.
3. A pamphlet, often expressing religious or political ideas, that seeks to persuade.
Volunteers handed out **tracts** on legal reform.

tribulation
trib yōō lā´ shən

n. Great trouble or suffering.
The daily threat of injury or death because of buried land mines is only one of the **tribulations** the Cambodian people live with.

vignette
vin yet´

n. A short sketch that provides a clear picture.
The movie begins with a series of **vignettes** about life in Los Angeles.

18A Finding Meanings

Choose two phrases to form a sentence that correctly uses a word from Word List 18. Write each sentence in the space provided.

1. (a) is one with a weak stomach.
   (b) is one who rules through guile.
   (c) A paramount leader
   (d) A squeamish leader

2. (a) A cache is
   (b) a small opening.
   (c) an area of land.
   (d) A tract is

3. (a) A memoir is
   (b) A malady is
   (c) a failed attempt.
   (d) a sickness.

4. (a) If something is combustible,
   (b) it is excessively harsh.
   (c) it is ineffectual.
   (d) If something is inclement,

5. (a) things that are unnecessary.
   (b) things that cause suffering.
   (c) Tribulations are
   (d) Vignettes are

6. (a) If something is paramount,
   (b) If something is indelible,
   (c) it is soon forgotten.
   (d) it is most important.

7. (a) A vignette is   (c) an opening.
   (b) An aperture is   (d) a source of trouble.

8. (a) A cache is   (c) a religious pamphlet.
   (b) something hidden away.   (d) A memoir is

9. (a) To rectify a piece of work is   (c) to draw attention to it.
   (b) To delegate a piece of work is   (d) to assign it to someone.

10. (a) A requisite item   (c) is one that cannot be forgotten.
    (b) A combustible item   (d) is one that is needed.

18B Just the Right Word

Improve each of the following sentences by crossing out the bold phrase and replacing it with a word (or a form of the word) from Word List 18.

aperture
cache
combustible
delegate
inclement
indelible
malady
memoir
paramount
rectify
requisite
squeamish
tract
tribulation
vignette

1. Mark Twain's writings contain numerous **short sketches that give a clear picture** of rural America.

2. Please **make the necessary corrections to** these figures and return them to me.

3. The French **people representing their country** were among the dignitaries who left early.

4. Whatever had been in the **secret hiding place** was gone when we opened it.

5. The kidneys are part of the urinary **system of the body.**

6. I was not happy when I discovered that the ink stain on my new pants was **impossible to remove.**

7. These humorous **personal accounts** of life in the White House were written by various employees of the president and his wife.

8. Sleeping bags and warm clothing are among the **things that are required** for a camping trip.

9. Oily rags are **quick to catch on fire and burn,** so dispose of them carefully.

10. The March weather was so **stormy and unsettled** that we took a bus to the museum instead of walking.

18C Applying Meanings

Circle the letter of each correct answer to the questions below.
Question may have more than one correct answer.

1. Which of the following describes a **tract**?
   (a) It can be read.
   (b) It can be walked over.
   (c) It can be diseased.
   (d) It can be concise.

2. Which of the following is a **requisite** for survival?
   (a) food
   (b) entertainment
   (c) shelter
   (d) water

3. Which of the following is a sign of **inclement** weather?
   (a) dark clouds
   (b) change in temperature
   (c) fair skies
   (d) gentle breezes

4. Which of the following is **combustible**?
   (a) gasoline
   (b) steel
   (c) paper
   (d) wood

5. About which of the following might you write a **memoir**?
   (a) slavery
   (b) life in ancient Rome
   (c) your schooldays
   (d) the outer planets

6. In which of the following might there be a **vignette**?
   (a) a movie
   (b) a novel
   (c) an agenda
   (d) an anthology

7. Which of the following might be in a **cache**?
   (a) fuel
   (b) money
   (c) food
   (d) grimaces

8. Which of the following would be **paramount** during a hurricane?
   (a) finding shelter
   (b) drinking lots of liquids
   (c) turning off the electricity
   (d) getting exercise

18D Word Study

Each group of four words below contains two words that are either synonyms or antonyms. Circle these two words; then circle the *S* if they are synonyms, the *A* if they are antonyms.

1. balmy	paramount	temporary	inclement	S	A
2. delegate	correct	divert	rectify	S	A
3. bequest	tract	pamphlet	cache	S	A
4. requisite	ordinary	necessary	squeamish	S	A
5. memoir	malady	ailment	epoch	S	A
6. paramount	realistic	indelible	fleeting	S	A
7. opening	cache	aperture	pittance	S	A

Complete the analogies by selecting the pair of words whose relationship most resembles the relationship of the pair in capital letters. Circle the letter in front of the pair you choose.

8. ANNOYANCE : TRIBULATION ::
   (a) order : anarchy
   (b) scolding : tirade
   (c) item : agenda
   (d) agility : stamina

9. DELEGATE : RESPONSIBILITY ::
   (a) pilfer : theft
   (b) immerse : water
   (c) smell : nose
   (d) confiscate : property

10. SQUEAMISH : FORTITUDE ::
   (a) irascible : patience
   (b) pungent : smell
   (c) enigmatic : mystery
   (d) prudent : prudence

aperture
cache
combustible
delegate
inclement
indelible
malady
memoir
paramount
rectify
requisite
squeamish
tract
tribulation
vignette

18E Passage

Read the passage below; then complete the exercise that follows.

Prairie Women

One day in 1975, Joanna Stratton was exploring the attic of her grandmother's house in Topeka, Kansas, when she came across a large **cache** of yellowing documents stored in boxes. They turned out to be handwritten **memoirs** describing life on the Kansas frontier from the 1850s to the 1890s. They had been collected by Stratton's great-grandmother, Lilla Day Monroe. She herself had experienced the joys and **tribulations** of frontier life when her family had moved from Indiana to Kansas in 1884, as the frontier period was drawing to a close. Her family settled in Wakeeney, on a treeless **tract** in the western part of the state. Monroe married and became an attorney; later, with her family, she moved to Topeka, where she practiced law and campaigned tirelessly for women's rights.

The hardships patiently borne by the Kansas pioneers remained fixed **indelibly** in her memory. By the early 1920s, Monroe became concerned that the vital role that women had played would soon be forgotten since no written record of their experiences existed. She decided to **rectify** that by collecting personal, written passages of Kansas women who still remembered those days. As word of her project spread throughout the state, more and more women responded until she had collected eight hundred first-hand accounts, filled with vivid **vignettes** of pioneer life on the Kansas frontier.

It was evident from these recollections that shelter was the **paramount** concern of new arrivals. For a family settling in the treeless western part of the state, a plow was the chief **requisite**. Drawn by oxen, horses, or humans, it prepared the land for farming and provided the only building material available—sods. These were solid blocks of earth cut from strips of soil that were used for the walls and roofs of the one-room frontier homes. Emma Brown of Mitchell County recalled life with her children in a sod house during a period of **inclement** weather when her husband was away on a cattle drive. The dirt roof leaked, soaking everything inside. "How happy we were to have the sun shine out again," she wrote. She tells how she and the children carried everything outside to dry. "But, alas," her account goes on, "the next morning the rain was pouring down again." It continued for another week.

Emma Louisa Smith of South Sappa Creek pointed out another problem caused by the lack of timber. "There was not a tree or even a bush in sight to furnish us with fuel." Fortunately, the early settlers discovered an unusual source—the dried dung of cattle and buffalo was both **combustible** and plentiful. The task of collecting it was one of the many that were **delegated** to the children. Emma Smith concluded that, "the sod house and cow chips were two great factors in making possible the settlement of this country at so early a date."

Despite the need for every pair of hands to do a share of the work, the children's schooling was not neglected. Those who could read and write taught their children at home. Later, when local settlers organized schools, Emma Handy conducted classes at Oak Creek in a dirt-floored schoolhouse built of sods. She wrote, "It had neither blackboard, teacher's desk, nor chairs. The seats were small logs split and supported by pegs." Two small **apertures** cut into one of the walls provided the only source of light. The dirt floor served as a chalkboard, with a long, pointed stick used to write letters and numbers.

Life on the frontier was not for the **squeamish**. There were no doctors, nurses, or hospitals. When women gave birth, usually no one but a neighbor was in attendance. With medical supplies difficult to obtain, **maladies** such as malaria had to run their course. Injuries were frequent, so residents in Kearny county were fortunate that a woman named Amy Loucks could act as surgeon when necessary. According to the account provided by her son, she closed wounds with fiddle string and a common needle. Once "with a razor and her embroidery scissors, she removed three fingers from the crushed hand of a railroad brakeman."

Lilla Day Monroe died in 1929 before she had completed her project. The manuscripts lay undisturbed in the attic of the family home for many years until Joanna Stratton came upon them. She had the pleasure of editing the writings and of bringing her great-grandmother's work to completion when, in 1981, *Pioneer Women: Voices from the Kansas Frontier* was published.

Answer each of the following questions in the form of a sentence. If a question does not contain a vocabulary word from this lesson's word list, use one in your answer. Use each word only once. Questions and answers will then contain all fifteen words (or forms of the words).

1. How does the passage indicate that Monroe remembered her early life?

2. Why would Stratton's book make interesting reading?

3. What were the minimum requirements for teaching lessons in school?

4. Why was the plow of **paramount** importance to settlers on the prairie?

5. Why do you think it was necessary to dry the cow and buffalo dung?

6. How do you know that the old papers Stratton found were a surprise to her?

7. What details in the passage suggest that the sod schoolhouses were rather dark?

8. How do you know that Amy Loucks was not **squeamish**?

9. What was one of the **tribulations** that the occupants of sod houses experienced?

10. How were most **maladies** treated by pioneer women?

11. How did Stratton **rectify** Monroe's failure to publish the book?

12. What is the meaning of **inclement** as it is used in the passage?

13. What were the sources for the information that appeared in Stratton's book?

14. Why do you think Stratton did not **delegate** the work of editing Monroe's papers?

15. What is the meaning of **tract** as it is used in the passage?

FUN & FASCINATING FACTS

The Latin *rectus* means "straight" or "right" and forms the root of *rectangle*, a shape made of four straight lines with four right angles. The Latin *ficere* means "to make" and forms the root of *factory*, a place where things are made. The two Latin roots combine to make **rectify**. When we rectify something, we *make it right*.

The French for "vine" is *vigne* and forms the root of the word **vignette**. The story of how these two terms came to be connected is an interesting one. It was once a common practice to place a decorative border on prints or the pages of books. The curling forms of grape vines and leaves along with clusters of grapes were often used for this purpose. These designs made little pictures in themselves. *Vignette*, therefore, came to be applied to any brief, descriptive sketch or a word picture.

Lesson 19

Word List **Word List** Study the definitions of the words below; then do the exercises for the lesson.

bulwark
bool´ wərk

n. 1. A wall-like structure used as a defense.
A wall of sandbags acted as a **bulwark** against the rising floodwaters.
2. A person or thing that protects or defends.
The Bill of Rights of our Constitution is a **bulwark** of our individual liberties.

culminate
kul´ mi nāt

v. To reach or bring to the highest point.
On the Boston Common, the Fourth of July celebrations **culminated** in a spectacular fireworks display.
culmination *n.* The result of a sustained effort; the high point or climax.
Winning three Olympic gold medals was the **culmination** of Florence Griffith Joyner's brilliant athletic career.

engulf
en gulf´

v. To swallow up by covering completely; to overwhelm.
During Hurricane Danny, a huge wave **engulfed** the boat and almost swept the crew overboard.

feasible
fē´ zə bəl

adj. Able to be done; possible or likely.
Building a new library is **feasible** provided that the town allots sufficient funds for it.

glut
glut

n. A much larger supply than is needed.
A **glut** of office space in downtown buildings resulted in a sharp drop in Boston's rents.
v. 1. To supply a much larger amount than is needed.
The weather was so ideal that California's growers **glutted** the market with strawberries.
2. To eat or consume to excess.
Sitting under the heavily laden branches, we **glutted** ourselves on ripe peaches.

havoc
hav´ ək

n. 1. Widespread destruction or devastation.
This morning we warily surveyed the **havoc** caused by yesterday's storm.
2. Great confusion.
When the rabbits escaped from their cages, they created **havoc** in Ms. Sweeney's classroom.

impregnable
im preg´ nə bəl

adj. Impossible to attack successfully.
The citadel was **impregnable** because of its hilltop location and strong defenses.

indefatigable
in də fat´ i gə bəl

adj. Not easily made tired; tireless.
Rescuers at El Teniente were **indefatigable** in their all-night efforts to reach the trapped copper miners.

onslaught
än´ slôt

n. A fierce attack.
The Union **onslaught** at Gettysburg stopped General Robert E. Lee's invasion of Pennsylvania.

phenomenon fə näm´ ə nän	*n.* 1. Any fact or event that can be observed or described. The aurora borealis, or northern lights, is a **phenomenon** visible in the night sky in the far north. 2. An unusual fact, event, or person. Publishing her first novel when she was eighty-five made her a publishing **phenomenon**. **phenomenal** *adj.* Extraordinary; very unusual. You must have a **phenomenal** memory to remember all those names after hearing them just once!
picturesque pik chər esk´	*adj.* Like a picture; pleasing or charming to look at. My favorite painting was of a **picturesque** old cottage with roses climbing its walls.
simultaneous sī məl tā´ nē əs	*adj.* Happening or existing at the same time. When the thunder and lightning are almost **simultaneous**, the storm is very close to you.
stipulate stip´ yōō lāt	*v.* To require as part of an agreement or contract. My lease **stipulates** that the landlord cannot raise the rent without giving thirty days notice.
susceptible sə sep´ tə bəl	*adj.* Open or subject to; easily influenced or affected by. Because I have hay fever, I am very **susceptible** to ragweed pollen.
wrest rest	*v.* 1. To pull away from with a twist. Tom **wrested** the ball from the player on the opposing team. 2. To take by force or as if by force. The military leaders **wrested** control of the government of Chile from President Allende.

19A Finding Meanings

Choose two phrases to form a sentence that correctly uses a word from Word List 19. Write each sentence in the space provided.

1. (a) Feasible events are those
   (b) that are copies of other events.
   (c) that occur at the same time.
   (d) Simultaneous events are those

2. (a) a fierce attack.
   (b) An onslaught is
   (c) A bulwark is
   (d) a demand greater than the supply.

3. (a) be overwhelmed by something.
   (b) To be indefatigable is to
   (c) To be susceptible is to
   (d) be easily affected by something.

4. (a) is as pleasing as a picture.
   (b) exists only in the imagination.
   (c) An impregnable place is one that
   (d) A picturesque place is one that

5. (a) To create havoc is to
   (b) To create a glut is to
   (c) cause a temporary shortage.
   (d) cause large-scale destruction.

6. (a) obtain it with force.
   (b) To wrest something is to
   (c) To engulf something is to
   (d) feed it more than it needs.

7. (a) something that cannot be explained.
   (b) something that offers protection.
   (c) A phenomenon is
   (d) A bulwark is

8. (a) A glut of something is
   (b) A culmination of something is
   (c) its low point.
   (d) an oversupply of it.

9. (a) To engulf something
   (b) To stipulate something
   (c) is to be protected against it.
   (d) is to insist on it.

10. (a) A phenomenon is
    (b) A culmination is
    (c) something unusual or extraordinary.
    (d) an unintended consequence or result.

bulwark
culminate
engulf
feasible
glut
havoc
impregnable
indefatigable
onslaught
phenomenon
picturesque
simultaneous
stipulate
susceptible
wrest

19B Just the Right Word

Improve each of the following sentences by crossing out the bold phrase and replacing it with a word (or a form of the word) from Word List 19.

1. The disagreements between players and management **reached the point of greatest intensity** in the 1994 baseball strike.

2. The Parents' Council's plan to raise scholarship money seems **likely to work** if everyone helps with the event.

3. Massive stones around the base of the shack made a **wall-like structure used for defense** against the shifting sand.

4. My grandmother was **unwilling to give in to exhaustion** in her efforts to earn enough money to send me to camp.

5. Rain in the desert is a **very unusual event** that shocks and pleases nomads.

6. Martina was such a strong swimmer that she escaped the wave that **swept over** her.

7. Ravi's little brother **took by force** the remote control from my hand.

8. Strawberry growers **produced more than met the need of** the market, so we got strawberries for dessert in our school lunches.

9. The sudden Red Sox defeat caused **a great amount of confusion** in the bleachers.

10. Peter's position on the chess board was **so strong that defeat was impossible**.

19C Applying Meanings

Circle the letter of each correct answer to the questions below. Question may have more than one correct answer.

1. On which of the following could one **glut** oneself?
   (a) food   (c) shelter
   (b) air   (d) exercise

2. Which of the following can be **simultaneous**?
   (a) two places   (c) two events
   (b) two names   (d) two sounds

3. Which of the following could cause **havoc**?
   (a) a reprisal   (c) a mutiny
   (b) a calamity   (d) a deluge

4. Which of the following would be **phenomenal**?
   (a) living to be one hundred   (c) shooting baskets
   (b) memorizing the Bible   (d) swimming the Atlantic Ocean

5. Which of the following could be **picturesque**?
   (a) a panorama of mountains   (c) a gruesome discovery
   (b) a pastoral painting   (d) a musical piece

6. To which of the following can a person be **susceptible**?
   (a) flattery   (c) suggestions
   (b) maladies   (d) entreaties

7. Which of the following can be **wrested** from someone?

(a) a rebuff

(c) a weapon

(b) control

(d) power

8. Which of the following is **feasible**?

(a) walking across the country

(c) controlling one's temper

(b) making a billion dollars

(d) running a car on water

19D Word Study

Complete the analogies by selecting the pair of words whose relationship most resembles the relationship of the pair in capital letters. Circle the letter in front of the pair you choose.

1. ANNOYANCE : TRIBULATION ::

(a) order : anarchy

(c) scolding : tirade

(b) agility : stamina

(d) aperture : window

2. IMPECCABLE : FLAW ::

(a) pungent : smell

(c) prudent : caution

(b) irascible : patience

(d) enigmatic : mystery

3. GLIB : SINCERITY ::

(a) despicable : dismay

(c) inane : sense

(b) affluent : wealth

(d) immaculate : forbearance

4. PATRIARCH : TRIBE ::

(a) accord : agreement

(c) president : company

(b) mind : intellect

(d) philanthropist : gift

5. INCESSANT : PAUSE ::

(a) interminable : end

(c) ineffectual : effort

(b) balmy : breeze

(d) lively : vitality

6. POISON : ANTIDOTE ::

(a) pain : agony

(c) disease : cure

(b) surmise : conjecture

(d) barter : trade

7. SIMULTANEOUS : TIME ::

(a) voluminous : volume

(c) identical : appearance

(b) rapid : speed

(d) abundant : profusion

bulwark

culminate

engulf

feasible

glut

havoc

impregnable

indefatigable

onslaught

phenomenon

picturesque

simultaneous

stipulate

susceptible

wrest

8. GLUT : SCARCITY ::
   - (a) tumult : turbulence
   - (b) banter : brevity
   - (c) affluence : poverty
   - (d) bulwark : protection

9. PUNGENT : NOSE ::
   - (a) colorful : eye
   - (b) strident : ear
   - (c) pale : skin
   - (d) interminable : time

10. DELEGATE : RESPONSIBILITY ::
    - (a) respond : question
    - (b) pilfer : theft
    - (c) immerse : water
    - (d) bequeath : asset

19E Passage

Read the passage below; then complete the exercise that follows.

The Thousand-Year Battle

What can a small country do if more than a quarter of its land lies below sea level, threatened continuously by inundation? How can it **wrest** control of the land from the sea so it can be used productively? For over a thousand years, the people of Holland have worked **indefatigably** to accomplish this task by building a system of dikes—great walls of earth and rock—as a **bulwark** against the sea.

In 1953, however, a freak combination of unusually high tides and hurricane-force winds along the southwestern coast caused this system to break down. Unable to withstand the storm's **onslaught**, many dikes gave way, allowing the sea to pour through. It **engulfed** the land, flooding 450,000 acres, killing eighteen hundred people, and driving thousands more from their homes.

The Dutch responded to this renewed challenge from the sea with the Delta Project, a plan to build a complex system of greatly strengthened dikes and dams whose most innovative feature was a gigantic barrier designed to seal off Holland's southern coast, the area most **susceptible** to flooding. Begun shortly after the 1953 disaster, the five-billion-dollar Delta Project took over thirty years to build and was opened officially on October 4, 1986, by Queen Beatrix.

To the Dutch people, the Delta Project seemed like the **culmination** of their thousand-year battle against the forces of nature. Having constructed an **impregnable** barrier against the sea, they could now declare victory. But within a very few years they realized that their reclaiming and use of the land had created other problems.

As far back as the fifteenth century, the Dutch had relied on pumps to remove water from the ground. The **picturesque** windmills so often associated with the Dutch landscape provided the power to operate these pumps. Modern technology provides more efficient methods, which the Dutch have used. The removal of groundwater, however, has lowered farther the level of the land, making it vulnerable again to flooding.

Simultaneously, another factor that has been noted worldwide in recent years is an elevation in sea level. This **phenomenon** is a result of what is known as the "greenhouse effect." Many scientists believe that carbon dioxide and other gases trapped in the upper layers of the atmosphere act like the glass in a greenhouse, permitting heat from the sun to pass through but preventing it from escaping. The result, these scientists believe, is global warming, which could melt polar ice, causing the sea level to rise two feet over the next hundred years.

The Dutch face other problems because of their intensive farming methods. They relied heavily on chemical fertilizers, which have played **havoc** with the environment, to such an extent that the stork, Holland's national symbol, has almost disappeared. In addition, the European Community, to which Holland belongs, faced with a **glut** of agricultural products, has **stipulated** that its members take fifteen percent of farmland out of production.

As a result of these pressures, the Dutch have arrived at a decision that once would have been completely unthinkable. Realizing that it was no longer **feasible** to continue such an extensive and unrelenting fight against nature, they have devised a plan that allows one-tenth of their farmland to revert to its natural state. Land once twenty feet below sea level that has been cultivated for a hundred years will again be under water.

Answer each of the following questions in the form of a sentence. If a question does not contain a vocabulary word from this lesson's word list, use one in your answer. Use each word only once. Questions and answers will then contain all fifteen words (or forms of the words).

1. What made the Dutch realize that the dikes were not **impregnable**?

2. How are the modern windmills the Dutch use different from the old-fashioned kind?

3. Why did the high tides and strong winds do so much damage in 1953?

4. What is the meaning of **bulwark** as it is used in the passage?

5. Do scientists think that the greenhouse effect explains global warming? Explain.

6. Why is Holland **susceptible** to flooding?

7. What did the Delta Project mean to the Dutch people?

8. What is the meaning of **phenomenon** as it is used in the passage?

9. How were the Dutch able to cultivate land that lay below sea level?

10. How does the passage suggest that the Dutch have worked tirelessly?

11. How effective were the dikes against the freak storm of 1953?

12. What happened to Dutch farms when the dikes gave way?

13. What is the meaning of **havoc** as it is used in the passage?

14. What contributed recently to keeping down the cost of vegetables in Europe?

15. What made Holland take farmland out of production?

FUN & FASCINATING FACTS

In Shakespeare's *Julius Caesar,* Mark Antony says, "Cry 'Havoc!' and let slip the dogs of war," as he realizes his assassination of Caesar will bring more bloodshed. This word has an interesting history. In Europe, during the early Middle Ages, when a band of robbers was about to lay waste to a village or other settlement, the leader would cry, "Havot!" This was the signal to start the attack. The word originated among tribes in Germany and meant "take by force" or "plunder." The result of such plundering was widespread confusion and destruction. The word, later changed to **havoc**, entered the English language by way of French and came to have its present meaning of "widespread devastation" or "destruction."

The Greek verb *phain* means "to appear." It forms the root of **phenomenon**, "an event that can be perceived by, or appears to, the senses." The correct plural of *phenomenon* is *phenomena*. (Among the *phenomena* we observed were an eclipse of the sun and a display of shooting stars.) Note, however, that in its meaning of "a rare or unusual event," *phenomenons* is also correct. (To have a musical genius in the family is rare, but to have two such *phenomenons* is almost unheard of.)

Lesson 20

Word List

Study the definitions of the words below; then do the exercises for the lesson.

alienate
āl´ yən āt

v. 1. To cause to feel unfriendly where friendliness once existed.
Unfortunately, the U.S. economic embargo against Cuba has **alienated** Canada.
2. To cause to feel alone and cut off from.
Her year out of school had **alienated** Ruby from her classmates.

fervent
fur´ vənt

adj. Having or showing great warmth or deep feeling; intensely eager.
Staring intently at the jury, Clarence Darrow made a **fervent** plea for his client's life.
fervor *n.* Great warmth and intensity of feeling.
Romeo addressed Juliet with such **fervor** that her eyes filled with tears.

forbearance
fôr bâr´ əns

n. A showing of self-control or patience.
With unusual **forbearance**, the principal asked the unruly student to explain the reason for his anger.
forbear *v.* To hold back; to keep from doing or saying something.
Mayor Lundgren asked the reporter to **forbear** revealing the information she had just heard until the news conference the next day.

gullible
gul´ ə bəl

adj. Easily tricked or cheated; too trusting.
I was **gullible** enough to believe him when he said he would call me.

hindrance
hin´ drəns

n. Any person or thing that is an obstacle.
Heavy traffic on the expressway is always a **hindrance** to my getting to work on time.

inflammatory
in flam´ ə tôr ē

adj. Causing anger or trouble.
Even though his rhetoric was **inflammatory**, the Supreme Court upheld his right to freedom of speech.
inflame *v.* (in flām´) 1. To excite or anger.
The management's refusal to hear them **inflamed** the striking electrical workers.
2. To make or become swollen and sore.
Try not to rub your eye; it will just **inflame** it.

ordain
ôr dān´

v. 1. To order or prearrange.
The U.S. Constitution **ordains** three separate branches of government: the executive, the legislative, and the judicial.
2. To install as a minister, priest, or rabbi, often in a special ceremony.
She hopes to work in the villages in Chiapas once she is **ordained**.

ovation
ō vā´ shən

n. An enthusiastic reception; long and loud applause.
When the pianist Leon Fleisher stepped onto the stage, the audience rose with a spontaneous **ovation**.

overt
ō vurt´

adj. Not hidden; public.
After years in hiding, members of the underground began to engage in **overt** acts of opposition to the Nazi regime.

recant rē kant´	*v.* To take back an opinion or statement; to confess to being wrong. After he talked to a lawyer, the young man **recanted** his confession and pleaded "not guilty."
rejoinder rē join´ dər	*n.* A reply to what has been said. The late comedian and actor Groucho Marx, one of the Marx Brothers, was famous for his funny, sharp **rejoinders**.
reproach rē prōch´	*v.* To find fault with; to blame. My mother **reproached** me for forgetting my little brother's birthday. *n.* Blame, disgrace, or discredit. When my grandmother died at the age of ninety-four, she had lived a life that was above **reproach**.
servile sur´ vīl	*adj.* Like a slave; excessively humble. Mark's **servile** attention to the boss made his coworkers very angry at him.
surpass sər pas´	*v.* To exceed or go beyond. The fact that Martha finished her first marathon **surpassed** her wildest dreams.
vilify vil´ ə fī	*v.* To make insulting remarks about; to slander. The candidates for governor agreed not to **vilify** each other in their commercials.

20A Finding Meanings

Choose two phrases to form a sentence that correctly uses a word from Word List 20. Write each sentence in the space provided.

1. (a) A servile person
   (b) is easy to like.
   (c) is easy to deceive.
   (d) A gullible person

2. (a) said as a response.
   (b) that stands in the way.
   (c) A hindrance is something
   (d) An ovation is something

3. (a) An inflammatory gesture
   (b) An overt gesture
   (c) causes a smile.
   (d) is one that is made openly.

4. (a) If you recant something,
   (b) If you ordain something,
   (c) you try to prevent it.
   (d) you take back your previous statement.

5. (a) an answer to something said.
   (b) a feeling of loneliness.
   (c) An ovation is
   (d) A rejoinder is

6. (a) rebuke that person.   (c) To reproach someone is to
    (b) gain that person's support.   (d) To alienate someone is to

7. (a) A servile remark is one that   (c) A fervent remark is one that
    (b) shows excessive humility.   (d) is irrational.

8. (a) say insulting things about that person.   (c) To surpass someone is to
    (b) To vilify someone is to   (d) fear that person.

9. (a) To alienate a group is to   (c) give it support.
    (b) To inflame a group is to   (d) lose its support.

10. (a) Forbearance is   (c) a belief that one cannot make mistakes.
     (b) Fervor is   (d) a willingness to live and let live.

20B Just the Right Word

Improve each of the following sentences by crossing out the bold phrase and replacing it with a word (or a form of the word) from Word List 20.

alienate
fervent
forbearance
gullible
hindrance
inflammatory
ordain
ovation
overt
recant
rejoinder
reproach
servile
surpass
vilify

1. My cut is becoming **swollen and sore** because I did not clean it well enough.

2. After Galileo said the earth revolves around the sun, church authorities forced him to **confess he was wrong.**

3. Ms. Hamilton's **expression of dissatisfaction** made me feel guilty that I hadn't practiced more.

4. "Programming a VCR **goes beyond** my understanding," my grandfather confessed.

5. Nelson Mandela's speech received an **enthusiastic reception** from the huge South African audience.

6. I'm much less **easy to deceive** now that I'm older and have more experience.

7. Coach Levine's half-time pep talk was so **deeply felt and expressed with such feeling** that it rallied the team and we went on to victory.

8. Whenever I read that column I have to try to **exercise self-control and keep myself** from writing an angry letter to the editor.

9. Senator Joseph McCarthy **made insulting remarks about** many innocent Americans.

10. Since Melissa has moved in with her grandmother, she doesn't seem to **go out of her way to be unfriendly to** people the way she used to.

20C Applying Meanings

Circle the letter of each correct answer to the questions below. A question may have more than one correct answer.

1. Which of the following **surpasses** a "good" rating?
   - (a) superb
   - (b) mediocre
   - (c) excellent
   - (d) poor

2. Which of the following might be a **hindrance** to a fast trip?
   - (a) a full tank of gas
   - (b) stopping for lunch
   - (c) a tune-up
   - (d) a flat tire

3. Which of the following can be **inflamed**?
   - (a) a wound
   - (b) a menu
   - (c) an interrogation
   - (d) a congregation

4. Which of the following can be **ordained**?
   - (a) a winter storm
   - (b) an execution
   - (c) a rule
   - (d) a rabbi

5. Which of the following might act in a **servile** manner?
   - (a) a sage
   - (b) a dignitary
   - (c) a patriarch
   - (d) a slave

6. Which of the following is an **overt** action?
   - (a) digesting dinner
   - (b) ordering dinner
   - (c) keeping a secret
   - (d) handing out tracts

7. Which of the following adjectives might be used to **vilify** a person?
   - (a) conscientious
   - (b) indefatigable
   - (c) exemplary
   - (d) inane

8. Which of the following statements could express **fervor**?

(a) "I know you can do it!"　　　　(c) "I adore Schubert."

(b) "Tell me about it later."　　　　(d) "I'll never make that mistake again."

20D Word Study

Match each definition in the lefthand column with the correct word chosen from the following list. Note that each word begins with the prefix *re-*, which can mean either "back" or "again." In the space next to each word, write the meaning of the prefix.

rebuff	resume	recant	recluse
recur	rejoinder	renounce	reprisal
reverberate	resilient	revise	reticent

Definition	**Word**	**Prefix meaning**
1. to start again after a pause	_____	_____
2. a funny comment meant as a comeback	_____	_____
3. heard over and over again	_____	_____
4. to drive back	_____	_____
5. to happen again	_____	_____
6. holding back from sharing one's thoughts	_____	_____
7. to take back what had been asserted	_____	_____
8. one who turns his back on human society	_____	_____
9. an act of striking back	_____	_____
10. to go over again and make corrections	_____	_____
11. able to spring back easily	_____	_____
12. to give up or turn one's back on	_____	_____

Read the passage below; then complete the exercise that follows.

Paul Robeson: All-American

In his 1958 autobiography, Paul Robeson tells of bringing home from school a test on which he had scored ninety-nine out of a possible one hundred. When his father **reproached** him for not getting a perfect score, Paul tried to explain that "no one ever gets one hundred." His father's **rejoinder** was a simple question: "Then why do they have it?"

Robeson's father had encountered and overcome great difficulties in his life. Born a slave in 1845, he escaped to freedom at the age of fifteen and joined the Union army at the outbreak of the Civil War. Later, he attended Lincoln University near Philadelphia, and was **ordained** a minister. At a time when African Americans were expected to be **servile**, Mr. Robeson was a strong advocate of racial justice and equality.

As he instilled a strong sense of purpose and principle in his eight children, he demanded much of them. Paul, the youngest, born in 1898, especially rose to the challenge. In 1915, he won a four-year scholarship to Rutgers College. However, as the third African American student ever to attend and the only one enrolled at that time, he felt **alienated** from his classmates. His presence on campus provoked both verbal and physical abuse from the more **overtly** racist students, but Robeson showed great **forbearance** in the face of these attacks. His response was to excel in everything he attempted. He won prizes for public speaking and served on the student council. He earned twelve varsity letters in football, baseball, basketball, and track. In 1917 and 1918, he earned a place on the All-American football team. He ended his final year with the highest grades of his graduating class.

Although he worked at various jobs, playing professional football and acting in plays on weekends to finance his education at Columbia Law School, Robeson practiced law only briefly, after graduation. He was hired by a white law firm in New York City, but the pervasive racism he encountered led him to abandon a career in which he believed he would be prevented from being effective. Instead, Robeson began devoting his time to acting in plays and giving concerts in which he sang spirituals, the traditional folk songs of African Americans. His rich, deep, expressive singing voice, along with the friendly, warm rapport he developed with his audiences, made him a successful and popular performer.

Within a few years Robeson's fame was worldwide. His performance as Othello marked the first Broadway appearance by an African American actor in the role. The production's 296 performances **surpassed** the record of any previous Broadway Shakespearean drama. Later, in *Show Boat*, when he sang "Ol' Man River" on opening night, the **ovation** he received was overwhelming; the song became forever associated with Robeson.

As he toured countries around the world, performing in concerts and the theater, Robeson recognized similarities between the struggles of poor working people in America with those of people in other countries. Along with his regularly scheduled concerts, he often gave additional performances with a low admission price, so that any who wished to hear him sing could attend. He refused to perform in theaters that had segregated seating. Through both song and speech he conveyed a message of peace, freedom, and racial equality for all peoples.

Throughout the 1930s and 1940s, Robeson was lionized wherever he went; tens of thousands of people attended his concerts. However, after World War II, Robeson was deeply disturbed by unfair treatment that he saw in his own country. Returning African American soldiers, who had fought for the freedom of European citizens, continued to be treated as second-class citizens when they returned to the United States. Robeson spoke out **fervently** against this, both in the United States and in other countries.

The United States government, regarding both his views and his words as **inflammatory**, acted. In 1950, his passport was confiscated. Robeson was **vilified** in the press as a Communist because of his political beliefs; he was called **gullible** for his continuing support of and friendship with the Soviet people. After these attacks, his popularity with American audiences declined sharply. He was forbidden to leave the country unless he **recanted** his political views. This he would not do. Concert halls, record companies, and television stations refused to have anything to do with him. These **hindrances** prevented him from continuing his life as an artist.

In 1958, his passport was returned, in part, as a result of pressure exerted by his supporters in countries throughout the world. Robeson was able to return to performing in concerts and to speaking his mind. He called his autobiography *Here I Stand*, and no one was ever in doubt where Robeson stood on the issues of racial equality and freedom.

Answer each of the following questions in the form of a sentence. If a question does not contain a vocabulary word from this lesson's word list, use one in your answer. Use each word only once. Questions and answers will then contain all fifteen words (or forms of the words).

1. What was Paul Robeson's father's **rejoinder** meant to suggest?

2. What is the meaning of **ordained** as it is used in the passage?

3. Why did the United States government object to Robeson's views in 1950?

4. What **overt** step did the United States government officials take against Robeson?

5. Would it be accurate to say the United States government and press treated Robeson with **forbearance** in the 1950s? Explain.

6. How do you know that Robeson was a great success in *Show Boat*?

7. Why would it be inaccurate to describe Robeson as uninterested in social issues?

8. What is one adjective that could not be used to describe Robeson? Explain.

9. Why was Robeson banned from foreign travel between 1950 and 1958?

10. For what did Robeson **reproach** the United States after World War II ended?

11. Why didn't Robeson practice law for very long?

12. How did the rapport between Robeson and his admirers change during the 1950s?

13. Why was Robeson **vilified** when he was a student at Rutgers?

14. Why would it be inaccurate to describe Robeson's father as **gullible**?

15. What might Robeson's father have thought of his son's accomplishments?

FUN & FASCINATING FACTS

Don't confuse **forbear**, which is a verb in which the accent falls on the second syllable, with *forebear*, which is a noun in which the accent falls equally on both syllables and which means "an ancestor." To complicate matters, the noun *forebear* is sometimes spelled *forbear*. No one ever said the English language was simple or logical!

The adjective **gullible** is formed from the verb and noun form *gull*. To *gull* someone is to deceive or trick that person; someone who is easily deceived is a gull. Both verb and noun forms are passing out of use, but there are still enough people capable of being easily deceived to keep the adjective form current.

Review for Lessons 17–20

Crossword Puzzle Solve the crossword puzzle below by studying the clues and filling in the answer boxes. Clues followed by a number are definitions of words in Lessons 17 through 20. The number gives the word list in which the answer to the clue appears.

Clues Across

1. To insist on as part of an agreement (19)

6. Something required or necessary (18)

7. To correct or adjust (18)

10. A fortress or stronghold (17)

11. Cold, wet, or stormy (18)

14. To involve in a conflict (17)

16. An opening or hole (18)

17. Abbreviation for *et cetera*

20. To swallow up by covering (19)

23. An extended period of time (17)

24. Widespread destruction (19)

25. Easily upset or made sick (18)

26. _____-turvy

27. Anything hidden or stored (18)

Clues Down

1. Showing exaggerated respect (20)

2. The male head of a family (17)

3. Of the same amount

4. To take back an opinion (20)

5. A short descriptive sketch (18)

8. Possible, reasonable, or likely (19)

9. To leave to others in one's will (17)

12. A stretch of land or water (18)

13. To get down on one's knees

15. To exceed or go beyond (20)

18. To obtain after a struggle (19)

19. A successful action (17)

21. An oversupply (19)

22. The two of them